Research Library
000796
D0296979

E.C.C.
RESEARCH DEPARTMENT
LIBRARY

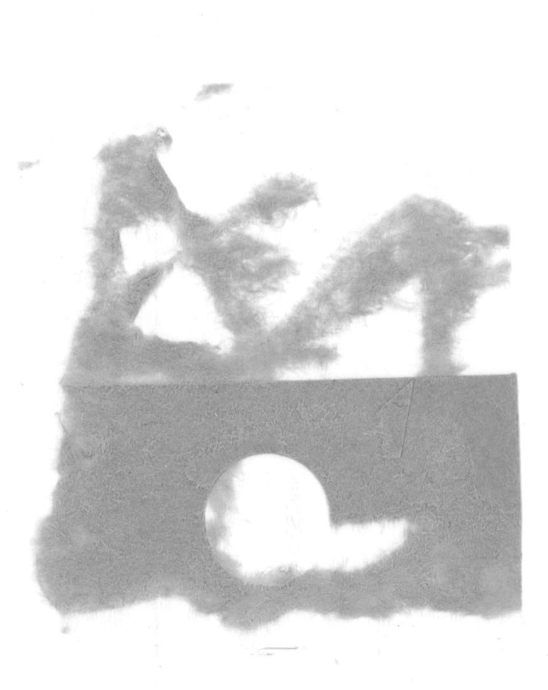

THE INTEGRATION
of Technologies

Technology, the science of industry, is subdivided into compartments, each apparently separate from the other. There are, however, common threads linking the individual technologies together and these links can provide a common body of theory and techniques which should be applied to many diverse industrial problems. The great importance of this point to modern industry has been appreciated by the Shell Chemical Company, who instituted an essay competition in collaboration with the British Association for the Advancement of Science around this central theme. These essays have been collected and edited by Leslie Holliday, Director of Carrington Plastics Laboratory ('Shell' Research Limited).

THE INTEGRATION of Technologies

edited by
Leslie Holliday
DIRECTOR, CARRINGTON PLASTICS LABORATORY
'Shell' Research Limited

HUTCHINSON & CO (*Publishers*) LTD. 178–202 Great Portland Street, London W.1

London · Melbourne · Sydney · Auckland · Bombay · Toronto · Johannesburg New York

First published 1966

This book has been set in Times New Roman type face. It has been printed in Great Britain by Benham and Company Limited, Colchester, and bound by Wm. Brendon and Son Limited, Tiptree, Essex

LESLIE HOLLIDAY

Preface

'The disposition to abstractions, to generalizing and classification' is 'the great glory of the human mind'. 'To generalize is to be an Idiot; to particularize is the alone Distinction of Merit'. The first was said by Sir Joshua Reynolds in his *Discourses*, the second was written by William Blake in the margin of his copy of Reynolds' book.* Although the context of these views is the visual arts, the conflicting states of mind which they express have been found throughout the ages and are found today for example in the sciences and in technology. It is this conflict within technology which is the starting point of this book.

All fields of intellectual endeavour need their generalists and their specialists, their Reynolds and their Blakes, their Einsteins and their Madame Curies. However, if a discipline or a technology is to progress, the two approaches must maintain a proper balance. Some are needed who will explore the frontiers of knowledge with a hand-lens (to quote Sir Eric Ashby), and others who will use a telescope. Some people believe that the hand-lens is too much in favour in the field of technology at the moment, and this book makes an attempt to redress the balance by searching for the common ground between different technologies.

The book has its origins in an essay award which was instituted in 1965 by Shell Chemical Company Limited, in collaboration with the British Association for the Advancement of Science. It is intended that this award should run for seven years, the central theme being *The Interaction of Technologies*. The topic was formulated as follows:

> 'It is acknowledged that there are divisions and barriers between different technologies at the moment and it is agreed that these impede scientific and industrial progress. We believe that there is more common ground between these existing technologies than is normally conceded.'

A selection of the essays submitted has been made for publication, in order to stimulate a wider public to think along similar lines. It is hoped that this selection, which examines the same problem from different viewpoints, will be of interest to many scientists, technologists and engineers in industry, as well as in universities and colleges of technology.

Three earlier papers, which bear on the same theme, have also been included. These were written by Professors Danckwerts and Toulmin, and myself. I am grateful to the editors of *Advancement of Science* and *Nature* for permission to publish the latter two.

*David Piper, *History of English Painting, 1500–1880.*

THE AUTHORS

1 PROFESSOR DANCKWERTS, G.C., M.B.E., has been the Shell Professor of Chemical Engineering at Cambridge University since 1959. His degrees were taken at Oxford University and the Massachusetts Institute of Technology. He was Deputy Director of Research and Development for the U.K. Atomic Energy Authority from 1954–6, Professor of Chemical Engineering Science at the Imperial College of Science and Technology from 1956–9 and has recently been President of the Institution of Chemical Engineers.

2 PROFESSOR STEPHEN TOULMIN is Professor of the History of Ideas and Philosophy at Brandeis University, Boston. He studied Mathematics, Physics and Philosophy at Cambridge and was a Fellow of King's College from 1947–51. He later taught philosophy at Oxford and Leeds Universities and as a visiting professor in Australia and America. He directed the Unit for the History of Ideas on behalf of the Nuffield Foundation from 1960–5. He has published books on moral philosophy and logic, and co-produced a book and film series on the development of scientific thought, but the main body of his work has centred on the interrelations between science, and history, philosophy, sociology and politics.

3 LESLIE WALTER BOXER is Counsellor and Head of the Technical and Economics Division of the European Nuclear Energy Agency, specifically interested in economic co-operation and development. After postgraduate work in Nuclear Engineering at Manchester University and Advanced Management studies at Harvard University he worked as an electrical engineer for Crompton Parkinson in the Plant and then Atomic Power divisions. His interests in this field have been particularly concerned with scientific and technical collaboration, the uniformity of approach in concepts of knowledge, and techniques for the teaching and transfer of information.

4 JACK BELCK is a graduate teaching assistant in journalism at the University of West Virginia, and has worked specifically on the various forms of written communication. He has also been active in educational broadcasting, free-lance and news writing and as a science editor.

5 DR. CARL HANSON is lecturer in Chemical Engineering at the Bradford Institute of Technology. After graduating in chemistry and chemical engineering he first managed the family chemical works, J. S. Hanson of Bradford, followed by a period in the research and development branch of the

Industrial Group of U.K.A.E.A., where he specialized in the problems of nuclear fuel processing, and, in particular, solvent extraction. He has since created a school for research in this field at the Bradford Institute. With a travelling scholarship awarded by the Goldsmiths' Company, he toured Europe studying methods of teaching chemical engineering, and has since interested himself in the need for more interrelated work in the region between chemistry and chemical engineering.

6 DR. R. A. COOMBE is Head of the Department of Electrical Engineering and Instrumentation (with Physics) at the Constantine College of Technology, Middlesbrough. His career has included a period as research physicist for the English Electric Co., and lecturing posts at the Stafford College of Technology and the Department of Electrical Engineering, Woolwich Polytechnic. The bulk of his work has been concerned with direct energy conversion (M.H.D. in particular), and with nuclear physics generally. He has published a book on M.H.D. Generation, and broadcast on Direct Conversion for the B.B.C. Science Survey Series.

7 ALEX L. MARSHALL is a graduate in Civil Engineering from the Royal Technical College, Strathclyde, and lectures in Civil Engineering at Sunderland Technical College. He has spent several years in the construction industry concentrating on hydro-electrical work and nuclear power.

8 DR. ALFRED M. PRINCE is with the New York Blood Centre, New York. His career has included a period of research and instruction at the Yale Department of Pathology and research in Virology whilst on military service in Japan. Later he became Associate Member of the Wistar Institute and Assistant Professor in Pathology at Yale. Apart from his present research work he has given considerable study to the technological and creative background to scientific research work.

9 D. M. JAMIESON is Chief of the Industrial Models Division of the National Energy Board Canada. He graduated in Mathematics and Physics and, with honours, in pure and applied mathematics from St. Andrews University, Scotland. He was plant statistician for the Ammunition Division of Canadian Industries Limited and also worked for the Canadian Defence Research Board. Later he was on the staff of the MITRE Corporation, Mass. and did graduate work at the Massachusetts Institute of Technology. He is a Fellow of both the Royal Statistical Society and the American Association for the Advancement of Science.

10 SIMON WOOLF is a consulting engineer (graduate of University College, London) and since 1957 has run his own practice, designing a complex variety of buildings and works. His design career includes two years with the Timber Development Association, whom he represented on an O.E.C.C. Productivity Commission, and a period with F. J. Samuely, consulting engineers. Apart from his work on the problems of design and construction, he is interested in the theoretical generalization of symmetrical and repetitive structures.

11 D. A. WALKER began his technological life with A.W.R.E. Aldermaston, devising and developing techniques and instruments for the measurement of radiation. He has spent the last nine years with Rolls-Royce Ltd., in a dual capacity: firstly as supervisor of the radioisotope applications department involved in much comparative exploration and research into alternative techniques, and secondly with responsibility for a Health Physics Service. He has been particularly concerned with technological aspects of the engineering industry.

12 DR. EDWARD MANOUGIAN is Research Associate in the Biochemical Division of the University of California. His experience has included five years of hospital work as Physician, Surgeon and Doctor followed by two years of postgraduate study in Mathematics and Statistics. As part of his present research he has published work in the field of C_{14} glucose kinetics in humans, its theory and applications.

13 DR. ARNOLD REISMAN is Visiting Professor of Engineering and of Commerce at the University of Wisconsin, Milwaukee. He has had much experience in both the industrial and academic fields of engineering. He spent two years with the Los Angeles Department of Water and Power, working on the design of major steam power plants, since when he has pursued an academic career as lecturer and professor (with the C.S.C.L.A. and other technological institutions), combining this with much consultant work on projects varying from water resource systems to weather research rockets.

14 LESLIE HOLLIDAY is Director of the Carrington Plastics Laboratory, 'Shell' Research Limited. He was a Harrison scholar, taking a 1st class honours degree in chemistry at Oxford. Since 1940 he has worked for the Shell Company in many parts of the world, in manufacturing (on both the oil and chemical sides of the business) and in research. He is a member of various government scientific committees, and President of the Materials Science Club. He is the author of papers on the history of materials, and materials science generally, and has recently edited a book on the subject, entitled *Composite Materials.*

15 DR. JOHN HEARLE is Reader in the Textile Technology Department of Manchester University and has worked in the Faculty of Technology at this University since 1949. His career has included visiting fellowships to the Massachusetts Institute of Technology and the Swedish Institute for Textile Research. Amongst his published works are many research papers and general articles as well as two books on various aspects of the textile industry.

1

PROFESSOR P. V. DANCKWERTS, G.C., M.B.E.

The Subdivision of Science

Viewed from Olympus, the realm of science would seem to be a continuum. Not only would all the branches of physical and biological science merge into one another, but they would seem to extend without break into other fields of knowledge and activity: into mathematics and philosophy; medicine and engineering; sociology; psychology and aesthetics.

For everyday purposes, however, the subdivision of knowledge is a practical necessity. So finely has the detail been developed in some fields of science that the area which a human brain can master in preparation for new discoveries must necessarily be small. Moreover, the administration of a continuum is impossible. Inevitably, both teaching and research in science are departmentalized in universities, and there are both physical and administrative barriers of varying heights between the different departments.

So much is inevitable; but we must not regard these interdisciplinary boundaries as more than a matter of convenience. They are arbitrary, often reflecting the initial growing points which arose naturally from human activities but which may not correspond with today's centres of scientific interest. One of the great problems of scientific administration is to provide the flexibility which will allow for constant shifts of emphasis and boundaries, and which will allow old subdivisions to dwindle as new ones form. If this is not done, if 'classical' subdivisions of science are allowed to become sacrosanct, we may find ourselves exploring a limited territory in ever-increasing detail instead of extending the frontiers.

New subdivisions of science arise sometimes from the growth and internal differentiation of existing domains, sometimes by the establishment of a new colony between existing frontiers. An example of the former is the differentiation of chemistry into organic, inorganic and physical, and of the latter, the establishment of biochemistry.

In industry and research institutes, the scientific continuum is apt to be sliced up in a different way from that which is traditional in the universities. When a practical problem has to be solved, a team consisting of representatives of several different 'sciences' must usually be formed to work on it. Sometimes these associations are transient, sometimes they give rise to viable new subdivisions of science. The association of scientists with practical engineers in industrial developments has given rise to the various branches of engineering science, while the practical requirements of medicine, agriculture, metallurgy, meteorology and so on have provided a number of sciences with sufficient individuality to be made manifest as university departments.

These new subdivisions are apt to encounter some resistance from the practitioners of existing sciences, who may feel either that their own field should be extended to cover the new requirements or that the new subject is merely a collection of odds and ends of different sciences, with no claims to be regarded as a 'unified discipline'.

However, the practical importance of these new subdivisions may be such that money is forthcoming to guarantee their establishment and independence, and history suggests that under the circumstances respectability is achieved in a generation.

Another way in which new subdivisions of science arise is through the influence of outstanding individuals. Dr. A may happen to be the first mathematician to turn his attention to helminthology. If he has 'green fingers' his intervention may prove to be practically fruitful and theoretically stimulating. He may in time become Professor A, first holder of the Chair of Mathematical Helminthology, head of a new department or sub-department, possibly with its own buildings and staff.

Dr. A may, of course, prove to have been unique in his interests and abilities; or he may have been no more than a brilliant salesman with a gift for attracting support. In either case his retirement will leave a white elephant on the scientific scene. Even among the long-established subdivisions of science, the prestige of a particular subject and its contribution to the general scientific fund may fluctuate widely with the emergence of able or colourful figures, their senescence and retirement.

The distinct emergence of a new subdivision of science is often marked by the appointment of a university professor or reader. Practice varies, but it would seem highly desirable not to attach inalienable specific titles to such posts. It is common enough to find that, in order to accommodate changes in scientific outlook, the chair of (say) Mathematical Helminthology has unobtrusively changed its function, and that it is nowadays invariably occupied by a geneticist. However, the existence of the title is always apt to be an encouragement to conservatism and to the perpetuation of a field of study which may have become of purely academic interest, at the expense of new developments.

It would be interesting to study in some detail the role played by bricks and mortar in determining or perpetuating the subdivisions of science. A massive, isolated building with an economic life of perhaps fifty or 100 years, and with 'Mathematical Helminthology' chiselled over the entrance, is a stabilizing factor of a kind which renders difficult any attempt at continued redeployment of resources to meet the changing climate of science. New buildings, with their practical and psychological advantages, attract students and research workers; there is never any difficulty in filling them. A new building is the visible sign of success in the power-play between scientists. It often serves to advise the world that an effectual figure has emerged to revitalize a particular branch of science. Buildings provide the visible memorial which many benefactors desire. Their availability and layout play perhaps as large a part as scientific conservatism in discouraging the regrouping and resubdivision of science. Each existing subject expands to fill the space available to it, and it is generally impracticable to take space from one of them and give it to an existing or projected rival.

There is no doubt that the boundaries of the subdivisions of science must continually shift as theoretical interest shifts to new areas of the continuum and as practical problems create new interdisciplinary groupings. The process of regrouping and of further subdivision must be catered for in any plans which are made for the development of science. It is equally certain, however, that this process will always be haphazard, subject to personalities, politics and the accidents of finance and building programmes. Any attempt at tight planning and control would be quite out of place in the jungle of science; there are, however, some steps which might be taken to provide the flexibility required by both individuals and institutions.

Although a considerable degree of specialization in university education is essential if superficiality is to be avoided, the object should be to produce graduates with an 'interdisciplinary' outlook. One way of doing this is to give the undergraduate an opportunity at least to 'minor' in some subject outside his own speciality. Research students might be more frequently encouraged to work on topics spanning the interests of two departments.

Flexibility may be more easily preserved in the university constitution if the titles of professorships can be conveniently altered as necessary, so that they can be conferred in recognition of emerging fields or the interests of outstanding individuals. Departments should be large, so as to include as large a slice of the spectrum as possible within a single administrative and physical boundary.

Departmental organization should be loose to avoid over-centralization. Anomalies should be regarded as normal. Interdepartmental enterprises in teaching and research should be encouraged. New building must be planned in such a way as not to fossilize the present subdivisions of science.

These ideas are not strange to English universities, but it is in the U.S.A. that they have been most consciously developed. New groupings of science into, for instance, Earth Science and Materials Science are foreseen. The Massachusetts Institute of Technology is currently conducting a radical investigation of the organization of science and engineering in a university, and the conclusions will no doubt find an application here, where the founding of new universities and the expansion of others provides an opportunity to establish the environment in which the subdivision of science will be least frustrating.

2

PROFESSOR STEPHEN TOULMIN

Science and Our Intellectual Tradition

In education, as in some other spheres of human life, the direction of our thinking is deeply affected by the system of general, unexamined assumptions characteristic of our day and age—what may be called our 'intellectual environment'. We swim, as it were, in a sea of 'common sense', and are carried along by it. And we are so little awake to its influence that we normally become aware of it only if we are swimming against the current.

Yet there are moments when we are made suddenly conscious of this environment: when we feel the shock of a new current and sense a change of direction—even a turn of the tide. And there are signs that, even now, we may be at such a turning-point: that in the second half of the twentieth century our intellectual environment may be very different from what it has been during the first half. To speak for the moment of education alone: for the past fifty years the flood tide of thought and practice in this country has been towards more intense and concentrated specialization; over the last few years there have been the first counter-eddies, and the voices of protestants have been taken seriously; while today we can feel in the undertow the first tug from a new direction, which may prove to be the beginning of a positively new current. There is at last a real drive to *re-integrate* the specialist disciplines—the so-called 'subjects'—into which our educational habits have become fragmented, and to set them working together in the service of a completer understanding.

This new current of thought is one which is making its force felt, not only in education but far more widely. Its influence can be observed all over the intellectual scene. Even in the fine arts, the 1960s have brought a similar change of tone. The early twentieth century has been a period of introversion in the arts, during which painters, poets and musicians have been preoccupied with their own techniques, valuing an abstract, analytical, craftsmanlike approach and turning away from emotion and representation. But now there is a general move to *reapply* these techniques (so skilfully sharpened and developed), and to re-create the artist's traditional worlds through new media and new instruments. The arts are becoming once again outward-looking, integrative. In politics, equally, the second half of the twentieth century surely promises to be very different from the first. We have lived through a period of rigid divisions, both in the domestic and in the international worlds: of parties representing sharply defined economic classes, of nation-states claiming absolute sovereignty—an age of self-determination, nationalism and particularism. Now there is obvious impatience, both at home and abroad, with class-parties and rigid nationalisms: the human race is searching after new modes of political union and integration, which will preserve the fruits of self-determination without complete fragmentation.

In the world of learning likewise (to come nearer home), university organization in Britain has been marked for fifty years by growing and deepening divisions between faculties, departments and other sub-units, all claiming the right to govern their own affairs—research, graduate and undergraduate teaching equally—for themselves. From being academies, our universities have been turning into mere federations. Indeed, the chief attraction to younger scholars of the new universities, such as Sussex, is not (as cynical Northerners declare) their sunshine figures and their proximity to London, but the way they are turning their backs on this fragmented faculty structure. For those who are interested in the *re-integration* of learning and education, the typical early twentieth-century British university has become an administrative dinosaur. Within some of the academic disciplines themselves, the new currents are already flowing strongly: in philosophy, for example. The predominant concern of Anglo-Saxon philosophy has for fifty years been technical, professional and inward-looking—the tone was set at the turn of the century by Russell and Whitehead's *Principia Mathematica* and G. E. Moore's *Principia Ethica*. Now there is a widespread desire to *reapply* the intellectual techniques so lovingly developed, and to put conceptual analysis to work on to larger, outward-looking problems. As for the natural sciences: Dr. Robert Morison described in a recent issue of *Daedalus* how 'the technology of data gathering and processing' was helping 'to free us from the burdens of specialization', and declared that: 'The splitting of our scientific culture into language blocs does not doom us to the splendid isolation of the Tower of Babel. The separate ways if pursued long enough can lead to an even more splendid and imperial synthesis of crystal clarity.'

In each case, there is the same desire not only to preserve the technical gains made during the last five or six decades—since the fruits of this analytic half-century have been admirable and valuable, whether in education, philosophy, the fine arts or the sciences—but to *exploit* them, by using them as the foundation for a reintegration of intellectual life, instead of allowing the arts and education alike to overshoot further into a parochial separation. The question facing us is, whether the new currents have enough power in them to become effective, or whether the drive towards the fragmentation of the intellect has acquired too much momentum to be reversed.

The choices before us can be illustrated most sharply and clearly in the natural sciences, and it is there that I shall begin by analysing them. For our educational quandaries are in many ways a microcosm reflecting the larger quandaries of science; and the same forces of disruption and reunification are at work in both areas. Nor are the choices entirely *novel* ones. Despite the secular self-importance which tempts twentieth-century man to believe that his problems are in every respect unique, the human race has been faced with similar choices before: notably, around the turn of our era, when the chief focus of intellectual life was finally transplanted from Athens to Alexandria. As I shall try to show, in fact, we are faced by a conflict between the Athenian and Alexandrian elements in our scientific tradition, and a great deal may turn on which acquires the mastery.

At the beginning of scientific thought, the central values of science were *intellectual* ones: 'Science began when men were perplexed', said Aristotle, 'A man who is perplexed recognizes his own ignorance. Thus, since men turned to science to escape from ignorance, their aim was understanding rather than practical gain.' This first great burst of scientific speculation, in Ionia, Southern Italy and Athens, was the direct offspring of a quite new confidence in the capacities of the human mind. Both in Babylonia and in Egypt, craft-knowledge and 'know-how' were in advance of anything the Greeks possessed—even in computational astronomy, so long as you wanted eclipse-predictions rather than theoretical understanding. But only in Greece were the traditional mythologies explicitly set aside: as Aristotle put it, 'It is not worth while scrutinizing the subleties of mythologizers. Instead, we must cross-question those who are prepared to offer arguments for their views.' And the resulting combination of free speculation and vigorous criticism carried the Greeks in 400 years from the first sweeping theories of Thales and Pythagoras to the exact and sophisticated analyses of Archimedes and Hipparchus.

At this point, the Greek scientists were trembling on the verge of modern science. If the ideas of Archimedes and Hipparchus had been thoroughly followed up, the conceptual innovations which were to transform astronomy and dynamics after A.D. 1550 (and through them all of science) might have occurred a millennium and a half earlier. What stopped this happening? This is a crucial question for our whole understanding of the development of scientific thought. I believe myself that the fundamental reason was a *failure of intellectual nerve*. The transition to Alexandria resulted in a general weakening of ambition: from being 'natural philosophy', science became a kind of intellectual technology. Hero's *Pneumatica*, for example, starts with a perfunctory statement of the atomistic theory of matter, but consists almost entirely of designs for hydraulic and pneumatic gadgets—including the first slot-machine (delivering holy water), and table-decorations for the dining-rooms of the rich, As for Claudius Ptolemy, the greatest astronomer of late antiquity: he could do his sums, make his predictions, more accurately than anyone else before Copernicus, but in matters of fundamental theory he was—quite explicitly—an agnostic. It was enough, he declared, for astronomers to concentrate on their calculations: there was no hope of humans here on Earth reaching agreement about the true structure and workings of the Heavens. Thus the big questions, on which science had flourished in the Athenian era, were set aside, and the confidence of the Ionians was disowned. Men returned to older dogmatic and mythological traditions, and the intellectual debate was fragmented into a Babel of sects and schools.

Conversely, in the sixteenth century, scientific inquiry at a really profound level revived, not because of some supposedly novel experimental method but because the old Ionian confidence had revived. Copernicus rejected Ptolemy's compromise, and demanded a theory of the heavens which would be consistent, systematic and convincing; and this same robust insistence on reality and consistency provided the main head of steam behind Galileo and the other 'New Philosophers'. Quotations from Francis Bacon might be useful as levers for opening a way into Charles II's Treasury; but otherwise they were 'strictly for the birds'—what men like Newton and Boyle were after was not doubling the hay-crop but a deeper theoretical grasp on Nature.

Science as we know it, then, is almost entirely the product of two periods of 400 years each, beginning around 550 B.C. and A.D. 1550 respectively. In both periods the mainspring of scientific progress has been philosophical, not technological. The questions about the scale and layout of the world-stage, which preoccupied Anaximander in the sixth century B.C., are still being argued between Fred Hoyle and Martin Ryle today. The basic Athenian puzzles about the fundamental dramatis personae of Nature are argued today by men like Werner Heisenberg and David Bohm. And problems about the time-scale and plot of the drama through which Nature unfolds, which were raised by Empedocles 500 years before Christ, are at issue again today when Urey and Oparin, Pirie and Bernal debate the origin of life on Earth. And all these large questions, which form the traditional core of 'science'—in its Athenian role of 'natural philosophy'—are directly and intimately connected with those questions which are fundamental to the 'humanities' also: questions about Man and his Place in the Scheme of Nature. It was this philosophical strand which, in earlier centuries than ours, made science so important for our wider culture also, so that Kepler and Galileo became dominant influences on Donne and Milton. Dryden and Pepys were quick to join the Royal Society, Voltaire and Goethe were fascinated (or repelled) by the intellectual implications of Newton, and Coleridge and Tennyson by those of Davy and Darwin. In each case, the Athenian impulses at the heart of modern science fired the imagination of the literary men in a way which would have been inconceivable if scientists had continued to accept the self-imposed limitations of Ptolemy and his fellow-Alexandrians. But in that event, of course, the Scientific Revolution would never have taken place either.

Against this background, the dilemma of present-day science is all too clear. By the 1960s, science is becoming increasingly subject to Alexandrian forces, and these are threatening to become dominant. More and more, it is being considered as an assemblage of skills—practical, technological skills, and theoretical, mathematical skills—rather than as 'natural philosophy'. On the theoretical side, there are echoes of Ptolemy's agnosticism in the belief (orthodox among quantum theorists) that questions about 'reality' and 'actuality' have become pseudo-questions, on which we must turn our backs. On the practical side, the sheer pressure of finance and patronage is siphoning off hands and brains into gadgeteering, most of it without serious hope of philosophical fruit. And it is only symptomatic of the present situation that men like Werner von Braun (the so-called 'space-scientists') can usurp a title belonging rather to the Ryles and Bohms and Bernals of our age. If Athenian considerations prevailed, our money would be going, not into the Moon-race, but into C.E.R.N., molecular biology, embryology, psycho-pharmacology and ethology—to say nothing of the other behavioural sciences, on which even the Royal Society still turns its back. As it is, there is a real danger that our new obsession with 'know-how' may stifle the natural philosophy from which it sprang. We can too easily delude ourselves into believing that unforeseen benefits to science will 'spin off' from space-adventures. There will be some dividends, surely: but these will not be in any degree commensurate to the expenditure of money and brains involved. For the hard fact is, that you can't spend the same money twice, both on the Moon-race and on real science, or employ the same Ph.Ds on two different jobs; and to find the prospective cost of a Man-on-the-Moon we must (as Dr. Warren Weaver has computed) deny ourselves a fantastic list of benefits, including generous fellowships for 50,000 scientists *a year*, a complete new university for every one of the fifty-three new nations, and three more Rockefeller Foundations. In short, our scientific tradition—the intellectual tradition, that is, which has been the mainspring of scientific thought—is rapidly turning into the Goose that laid the Golden Eggs. It is becoming the victim of its own success.

If one turns to education, similar conflicts and dangers are immediately apparent. The first half of the twentieth century has bred in the teaching world the same preoccupation with skills, techniques and know-how, the same neglect of general ideas, critical understanding and the intellectual tradition, that it has in our attitudes to science. In this respect (as I said earlier) educational trends have only reflected the wider tendencies of our age.

One stereotype, in particular, has bedevilled much of our recent thought about education; and in its own way this conception is a typical product of the past half-century's intellectual environment. For the whole discussion has tended, more and more, to accept without scrutiny 'nationalistic' claims by the different academic 'subjects' to be autonomous, self-determining entities, each with absolute sovereignty over its own territory. One direct by-product of this stereotype has been the protracted debate about the 'gulf' between science and the humanities—a debate which takes it for granted that these two academic territories have no common ground. It would be less misleading to think of the various subjects as different approaches to (and departures from) the common core of questions and ideas which originally formed the intellectual tradition of Europe, and is now shared by the whole world. Since one stereotype can be displaced only by another, a new picture is required: we should think of the different academic subjects not as separate entities but as the segments of a fan, overlapping at the centre but branching off from there in different directions—or perhaps, better still, as the different branches of a tree, which have all sprung (and all draw their life) from a common trunk.

To follow up these new images: the overlapping region—the common ground, or common trunk, which all the subjects share—is the central core of ideas on which they all alike have a bearing. The separate segments, or branches, are the special techniques, concepts and skills which they have developed in dealing with these ideas. Thus science unites the tradition of natural philosophy with a collection of mathematical and manual skills; history, beginning as a perspective on human affairs, has developed its own techniques for handling pipe-rolls and Parliamentary records; English, French and German, starting from a concern with the intellectual traditions of Britain and Europe, have elaborated their own ranges of linguistic, phonetic and critical skills—to the extent of inventing, in e.g. dialectology, sciences potentially more narrowing than any of the natural sciences. And when one compares these different combinations, the justice of the new images becomes clear; for the bodies of general ideas in all these subjects are related to one another far more closely than their different skills and techniques.

Historians, scientists and linguists alike are proud of the intellectual techniques which they have spent the last half-century sharpening up, and rightly so. We cannot afford to undervalue these techniques, since they represent the proper contribution which each subject can make to the progress of our common intellectual debate. But they derive their sap, value and interest—in short, their intellectual *justification*—from their connexion to a central body of general questions and ideas. They are all instruments of thought, not self-sufficient ends. Unfortunately, several factors have conspired in recent decades to drive the various academic subjects apart; and it is these *centrifugal* forces which have produced the illusion that the academic disciplines are distinct and independent entities. Throughout the educational world, there has been a growing preoccupation with techniques and skills, which has turned men's attention away from the common questions linking the different foci of study. So, by now, many scientists (and science teachers) have ceased to think of their specialities as parts of the mid-twentieth-century cross-section of a developing tradition, already 2,500 years old; many historians (and teachers of history) no longer concern themselves with any overall perspective of human affairs; and so on, and so on. . . . Gulfs have opened between all our subjects *as taught and examined*, which have no place in the field of learning as a whole.

Some of these centrifugal factors are respectable enough. The very creation of academic professions, for instance, is largely a twentieth-century phenomenon; and with the rise of these new professional groups ('scientists', 'philosophers', 'modern linguists', etc.) there has been a natural, and proper, interest in professional techniques, so that the intellectual instruments of each subject have become ends as well as means. Along with this has gone a less admirable kind of 'professionalism': a certain academic nationalism or particularism, with every subject demanding to be master in its own house, instead of co-operating in a joint intellectual quest. (The federal structure of present-day British universities is a product of this attitude.) But the most powerful of the centrifugal forces have probably been the practical and administrative ones. In an age of massive educational expansion, we have naturally been tempted to concentrate on the aspects of education which can be taught, learned and examined most easily and straightforwardly.

This temptation has, by itself, done a great deal to distract education away from general ideas and critical habits of mind, and towards the inculcation of skills and abilities. For it is a comparatively straightforward matter to impart the ability to solve problems in Newtonian dynamics, or techniques of scansion and critical analysis, or the capacity to translate a foreign text (more or less) or to repeat historical facts. It is a much more demanding task to get across to your class an understanding of the *significance* of those skills, or the *point* of the techniques. To explain what difference the Newtonian theory has made to all our outlooks is, surely, a legitimate and interesting problem in physics: yet it cannot be done with the help of calculations alone—instead it calls for a deeper and more critical kind of thought, together with the power to express oneself cogently in the common language of educated men. Yet it must be remembered that, for Newton's contemporaries and immediate successors, this deeper significance was the really exciting thing. When Edmund Halley wrote his *Ode to Newton* for the second edition of the *Principia*, for instance, he quoted as Newton's supreme achievement not his invention of a new kind of sums ('A perfectly-smooth elephant of negligible weight slides down an inclined plane', etc. etc.), but his demonstration that the appearances of comets were governed by intelligible mechanical principles:

> Now we know
> The sharply-veering ways of Comets, once
> A source of dread, nor longer need we quail
> Beneath appearances of bearded stars.

Newton's theory had been more than a mathematical innovation. It had been a master-stroke of natural philosophy; and, as a result, we could all of us—mathematicians and laymen alike—sleep easier at nights, and feel more at home in Nature.

Faced with tens of thousands of G.C.E. candidates a year, what have the Joint Matriculation Boards done? Their task has been to grade the performance of these children quickly, accurately, numerically and equitably; and to satisfy themselves that the marking of different examiners, and groups of examiners, was strictly and fairly compared. For understandable reasons, they have taken the easy way out. Skills and factual knowledge are easy enough to test by a written examination, and performance can be numerically graded. Understanding and critical ability call for a more discriminating type of examination, and do not lend themselves so readily to numerical grading. (The old *viva voce* methods, with an 'A, B, C, D, E' grading, were in some ways better designed for this purpose, and are still used by some continental countries, in examining for the *Abitur*—their counterpart of the G.C.E.) With the passage of time, the School Certificate and G.C.E. examinations have become almost entirely tests of formal skills, capacities and abilities, as contrasted with a deeper intellectual grasp and powers of expression.

What, then, is the missing element in our education today? Too often it is a sense that the things being taught, learned and examined are living parts of a larger, developing unity—that is, of our intellectual tradition. Until the turn of the century, this sense of our tradition could be taken pretty well for granted, and did not have to be insisted on. Every educated man was familiar, in outline at any rate, with the main skeleton of European thought. (His picture might allot more space to Horace and less to Aristotle than we should now think just; but all the main figures would be there in roughly their right relations.) Nowadays, when this sense cannot be taken for granted, it is the last thing children are given, the last lack to be made good.

Students of science can leave school skilled *performers* at all the techniques of their subjects, yet devoid of deep *understanding*, even of their own professional skills: they can reach the university believing that Newton lived in the nineteenth century, and that all theories dating back to before 1920 were the results of sheer incompetence. Nor are the scientists alone affected in this way: students of other subjects equally are trained in specialized skills, but given no grasp of their wider significance. They can analyse and criticize Blake's verses and Goethe's prose-style—but it is news to them that Blake and Goethe were both profoundly influenced by (and hostile to) the Newtonian view of Nature —'Newton? That's *physics*, surely!' If anything, 'English literature' is probably the subject least far gone towards mere technique, least completely detached from our traditional culture. Yet even this fact has its own incongruous consequences. The understanding of all our culture has become, in the eyes of some critics, one more literary technique: Raymond Williams, reviewing Jacques Barzun's latest book, claimed the analysis of key-notions in the history of ideas as the preserve of 'English', and Dr. Leavis expounds an arguable view of Man's Place in Nature and Society under the guise of a technique of literary criticism.

Yet, if our academic subjects are really branches growing from a common tree, we cannot afford any longer to close our ears to the discussions in other people's classrooms. Whatever our specialities, we must recognize that we are all in the same Academy, sharing in a common intellectual debate. In that case, our different disciplines are not separate fields of study, which need to be joined artificially, by 'gulf-bridging': they have their own natural unities, since they share an ancestry and their fields of concern overlap. And in that case, also, the *topology* of all our educational problems (so to speak) will be altered.

Much of the current passion which is spent attacking and defending 'specialization', for instance, results on this view from cross-purposes. Those who consider that the present degree of specialization in schools is excessively narrowing are not attacking the same thing that those who defend 'study in depth' are anxious to preserve. No one (least of all Mr. Peterson) need deny the value of discipline, rigour and connected study—all those fruits which Lord James claims for a coherent and concentrated field of interest: but, in return, Lord James must allow that any given subject can be studied in breadth as well as in depth—and should include serious attention to its role in our general intellectual scheme, as well as its own private skills and specialist techniques. (This is the significance of the 'Sussex doctrine', which presents students with a coherent group of subjects, *both* in depth *and* with a sensitive awareness of interrelations and the common tradition.) Much of the current passion about C. P. Snow's 'two cultures' is also, on this view, misplaced. Snow, was, of course, not *asserting* that the sciences and the humanities have separate and distinct intellectual ancestries and traditions, but *denying* this; and deploring the fact that today's educational methods leave people trained in the skills of one academic faculty or another, but equally unaware of the common traditions they share, and of the mutual relevance of their own subjects.

All the same, it is easier to diagnose than to prescribe. It is one thing to recognize that the emphasis in our educational system needs to be changed in a way which can reawaken understanding of our common intellectual traditions and so reunite our fragmented culture. Actually to take the practical steps required to adapt our educational processes to this need is quite another matter. The educational machine has tremendous inertia (in the physical sense): once it has started moving in any given direction, it acquires enormous momentum, and can be redirected only with a great expenditure of effort. The new currents in education, which could lead to the desired reunification, will not be able to establish themselves unless we do something to clear away the sandbanks laid down during the first half of this century. Instead, they will dissipate themselves in a mere eddy, while the main stream of educational practice continues to flow along the deep tidal channels scoured out by fifty years of ever-narrower and more technical specialization.

At the heart of our practical quandary remains the problem of examinations. If, as I argued earlier, 'every generation gets, in the long run, the kind of science its paymasters are prepared to finance', so now we can add as a corollary, that 'every generation gets, in the long run, the kind of education its school-leaving examiners are prepared to reward'. The present fragmentation of our culture will persist for just so long as the G.C.E. system remains geared-up to test for skills and factual knowledge rather than for understanding and a grasp of general ideas. It is not enough for Matriculation Boards to exhort teachers to watch their pupils' English expression and powers of criticism: until the Boards resolutely enforce demands for adequate intellectual grasp lucidly expressed—to the point of failing mere performers, however skilled—the general run of schools will have no sufficient motive for taking on the admittedly harder aspects of education.

Are the existing Joint Matriculation Boards capable of mending their ways? I sometimes doubt it. Perhaps it is no good looking to them for the new attitudes we need. Probably the only hope lies in some novel examining body (say, a New Universities Matriculation Board), which will be prepared to create from scratch the educational machinery that the second half of the twentieth century will require.

More is at stake in this problem than mere scholastic organization. For the future of our science, and of much else, will depend on the intellectual attitudes of the next two generations. Already (as I have argued) the Athenian attitudes of mind, whose critical probing and speculative freedom have been the stimulus of scientific growth both in the Ancient World and since the Renaissance, are under heavy pressure from the Alexandrian forces of the mid-twentieth-century. In the face of these pressures, they can be helped to survive only by a reunited and well-directed educational system. Another full century of the intellectual tide which has been flowing for the past fifty years could wash this tender (and temporary) growth away, and lead to a permanent fragmentation of our traditions—such as occurred in Alexandria. And if the Athenian elements in our science and culture were finally to be overmastered by the Alexandrian elements, which are very strong today, that would indeed be the onset of a new Dark Ages.

3

LESLIE WALTER BOXER

Self-Knowledge and Historical Perspective in a Science-Conscious Society

The conjunction of a rapidly increasing interest in the role of science and technology in modern society, and the relative multiplicity of practitioners in the field today compared with only forty or fifty years ago, means that it is becoming increasingly difficult to say anything new when attempting to explore a topic as complex as the interaction of technologies. Notwithstanding this early warning of a dearth of originality, I feel compelled at the outset to restate the basic tenet—however trite—that the eternal riddle of the relationship between the forces within Nature and the forces within Man has never been more pertinent in the history of human civilization than today, when we find ourselves precariously balanced at the fulcrum between man-manipulated natural forces of immensely constructive and destructive potential.

It is also general knowledge that, until recent times, discoveries of the nature of our environment and the evolution of scientific thinking had had relatively little impact upon the organization of society, and that changes which resulted in human attitudes over the centuries were confined to minority groups consisting chiefly of natural philosophers and theologians. With the advent of the Industrial Revolution, the expansion of manufacture and trade—stimulated by frequent wars—the situation changed rapidly in those countries whose political institutions and whose resources in manpower and materials were in a balanced relationship for such development.

These facts have long been recognized and need only to be repeated to emphasize the fact that industrial civilization has already passed the era when man's growing knowledge of the eternal forces of nature was still in step with his capacity to relate the implications of such knowledge to his contemporary needs. Today it is generally conceded that knowledge and capacity are very much out of step, and that the individual—whether scientist or layman—is beginning to experience a growing sense of personal impotence in attempting to adapt to the current avalanche of scientific and technical knowledge, and a growing concern over the great tracts of isolation which now appear to exist between areas of intellectual activity.

* * *

Unfortunately the fragmentation of scientific thought and activity cannot be conceived in such a way that the pattern presents itself as a rough jigsaw puzzle, where it is only necessary to relate the boundaries of the fragments to each other in order to perceive the correspondence between their profiles. Obviously, discoveries are yet to be made, and these may alter the intellectual shape of many areas of scientific study, and reveal fundamental links which were previously unsuspected, as was the case in the relationship between physics and chemistry in the nineteenth century, and as is now the case with chemistry and biology. The absence of such links, therefore, constitutes a series of gaps in knowledge rather than barriers or divisions between branches of knowledge and practice. On the other hand, there is good reason to suppose that the barriers which have become insinuated today between various branches of scientific activity have their origin in human weakness rather than in the incompleteness of human knowledge of the natural order.

Even the most cursory examination of the history of science and natural philosophy, or even a moment's reflection upon the undeniable unity of man's natural environment will reveal the falsity of denying the principle of common ground between all branches of science and their application in the technologies. It becomes immediately evident that, only in recent times has the growing body of scientific discovery and application made it increasingly difficult, and finally impossible, for any single individual to practice science to the full extent of contemporary knowledge, as was feasible for his historical predecessors. The subdivision of learning then appears in its true perspective as a purely arbitrary expedient to enable groups of individuals to concentrate in depth upon a programme of training and practice in a particular branch of science. Such composite vertical burrowing in the pursuit of specialized knowledge, however necessary it may be to respond to particular social, economic or political pressures, must inevitably be achieved at the expense of the broader or more horizontal perspectives of learning. It is, moreover, a perfectly natural consequence of this situation that specialists should develop a strong territorial affection for their own particular field of study, and eventually should feel the necessity to shield the structure of their speciality by an arbitrary territorial limit, thus introducing the concept of barriers between technologies. This leads to the inevitable conclusion that in any examination of the interaction of technologies, a good deal of attention should be given to the interaction of technologists, both within the scientific community and with society in general. It might, therefore, be more profitable to place a special emphasis upon the complex humanistic elements of this particular situation, rather than to attempt to reiterate the common scientific principles which underly all technological activity, and thus arrive at purely abstract conclusions.

Before doing so, however, it would be relevant to draw attention to two important new areas of scientific observation and application which have been given little opportunity so far to participate in the technological interaction. It is astonishing to observe the comparative isolation from classical science and technology of the knowledge gained in the workings of the conscious mind and of the revelations of man's role as a rational being. Such knowledge is in fact the key to understanding the extent of human capacity for objective evaluation of the significance of scientific thought and discovery, and provides some insight into the human motivations which throughout the recorded history of man have permitted the co-existence of myth and reality within the individual skull. The second area of observation which has been largely disregarded by the scientific and technological community is the knowledge and experience gained in recent years of the forces which control and influence the development of society, and which provide the essential background for the planning of painless evolution.

Thus there are two technologies which have largely been missed out of the interaction altogether, namely psychology and sociology, which could otherwise reveal the way to self-knowledge and illuminate the collective behaviour of human beings in their social environment. This is a paradoxical state of affairs in a period in which there are frequent professions of awareness of the narrowness of mind and prejudice engendered in us by our educational and social background. Is it not likely then that man is often attempting to exercise judgement of highly skilled mind over matter without a fuller understanding of the mechanism of individual human judgement and of the social environment?

If then it may be postulated that the present impression of discontinuity of contact within the scientific and technical community is a purely behavioural phenomena, then it may be relevant to attempt an appraisal of the fundamental influence exerted by the current thinking habits acquired by scientists and technologists.

* * *

It is facile to assert that the instinctive human regard for the preservation of the intellectual and material interests of the individual is the root cause of the formation of autonomous professional clans, which are uniquely absorbed in the importance of their own affairs, and interested in their relationship with other clans primarily with a view to preserving relative status. This platitude misses the essential problems, firstly, that for practical reasons arising from human limitations, recent advances have made it essential to provide autonomy in different branches of science in order to achieve a desirable degree of organizational efficiency, and, secondly, that practically all professional groups today are faced with overwhelming difficulties in communication not only between other specialized groups but within their own speciality. Then there is the perpetual difficulty of determining the optimum proportion of total working time which can and should be devoted to keeping up-to-date, even within a limited field, and the way in which such time can be spent to the best advantage. A great deal of discrimination is now needed to discern the personal usefulness and relevance of the enormous amount of material which is now available through the media of publications and organized meetings.

Some progress is being made on the physical problems of information retrieval and information transfer, but this progress will always be bounded by the finite limits of human ingenuity. In any event, the acquisition of more and more factual knowledge in itself is unlikely to foster a spirit of common identity among the host of practitioners of the many specialities. If it were possible to sum up the inestimable number of gaps in knowledge and understanding between individual people with a similar tradition of scientific training and discipline, the total might even surpass in magnitude the much publicized single gap between science and the humanities—which have recently been presented as the 'two cultures'—and where again the recognition of the inherent problems does not seem to have progressed much beyond general expressions of awareness, to the accompaniment of a good deal of unconstructive argument.

The very terms 'science' and 'the humanities' in themselves are a typical demonstration of human wilfulness in creating distinctions in fields of learning. 'Science' has been adopted as a convenient term for grouping the manifold studies of animate and inert matter, and the forces which influence its behaviour, and 'the humanities' has become an equally convenient term for grouping the branches of study of human activities throughout the history of mankind. But is it not beyond the bounds of human capability to assert that these two arbitrary concepts are entirely unrelated and can never become integrated within a continuous intellectual perception of reality?

It is inevitable, therefore, that the territorial limits resulting from our present basic thinking habits should be manifested in a certain lack of communication between many of our institutions. Indeed, contemporary psychological attitudes amongst many practitioners of science and technology probably present the most formidable problem in the effort towards achieving greater unity in these fields. We have long reached the stage where it is necessary to remind ourselves that science, technology and the humanities must be maintained as branches of learning, and must not deteriorate into becoming attitudes of mind.

* * *

Perhaps the most obvious example of intellectual apartheid is the rigid distinction which is still being made between scientists and engineers or technologists. The situation is aggravated to some extent by the unfortunate connotation of scientific activity into the categories of 'pure' and 'applied', from which the inference is often drawn that exercise in the abstract field is an intellectually clean occupation relative to a supposed vulgarity associated with practical activity, particularly where commercial considerations are predominant. The root of this distinction can probably be traced back to more than 150 years ago when craft technique first began to be employed on an industrial scale in advance of the direct application of science, so that technology originally became established in industry as practical craftsmanship with very little tradition of intellectual training. The scientific approach was most likely regarded with some suspicion, and was only adopted to the extent that it was able to produce a practical and profitable result.

It is understandable that in such circumstances, scientists would feel that the aims of industry would have little real connexion with the aims of science, and that industry would in fact tend only to impose restrictions on scientific intellectual liberty. Times have changed, however, and with the enormous growth of competitive industry, the evolution of skilled industrial workmen from artisans and craftsmen to engineering scientists and technologists has been every bit as rapid as the general evolution in scientific knowledge. Furthermore, the training of engineers in the technological applications of science has become just as rigorous as that of scientists, who can now no longer claim a monopoly over objective and creative thinking, nor can justify an attitude of condescension towards the more pragmatical aspects of their art. Nevertheless, as we all know, the academic isolation of the scientist from the engineer, however unrealistic and harmful to social development, still persists in 1965 and is actually fostered by a cult of puerile snobbery, in which cherished legend persistently triumphs over reality. The outdated images of white coat and greasy overalls, intellectual and non-intellectual, are still unconsciously or even consciously preserved, encouraged perhaps by a pseudo-aristocratic and anachronistic attitude towards the 'anathema' of the Industrial Revolution.

Social distinctions between scientists and technologists today are just as artificial as any such distinctions have always been between composers and musicians, playwrights and actors, sculptors, painters and architects or in any field which requires the duality of origination and interpretation for its expression. The one is the essential complement to the other, and there is no foundation whatsoever for any kind of distinction which attempts to compare different strains of mentality of equal quality, but trained in different orientations. In spite of the diffidence which still surrounds the mention of the whole delicate question of class relations in Britain, the social image of applied science could well be a significant factor in explaining why so many engineering places are now going begging in such British universities as provide them.

In effect, then, the professional engineer in modern society is still classified by many people as being associated with craft industry with a non-scientific tradition, and indeed he still shares the generic title 'engineer' with today's skilled or semi-skilled artisan who has not sought the rigorous educational training and intellectual discipline necessary to achieve professional competence. The situation is now further complicated by the introduction of a new category of specialists, the 'technicians', whose function and formation lie somewhere between that of the two arbitrarily defined 'engineers', although there is no reason to suppose that their relations with professional engineers cannot be modelled upon those developed between fully qualified specialists and their technical assistants in other professions, as, for example, in medicine. In Britain, recognition in terms of a more prestigious title such as 'chartered engineer', and more enlightened teaching to place the functions of the professional engineer in perspective with those of people of lesser skill and training but who are nevertheless free to borrow the same title, may help to raise the status of the engineering scientist in the public mind. The recent decision to grant fellowships of the Royal Society to more engineers and applied scientists generally is a welcome recognition of the overall contributions of technology to the advancement of science. Nevertheless, the social nuance still continues to be an insiduous element in the pseudo-intellectual flux of human motivations which tend to isolate scientists and engineers from each other.

* * *

The seriousness of all the psychological obstacles which block incentive towards free communication should not be underestimated in any attempt to reconcile the two camps of abstract and practical activities. How then will it be possible for both sides to arrive at a mutual understanding at the individual level, of the problems encountered in these two aspects of scientific activity, and to gain an appreciation of the nature of the creative thinking which has to be applied in order to make their particular contributions to progress? There is, of course, excellent scope for improvement in interdisciplinary relations in many large research establishments where closely co-ordinated team-work between scientists and engineers is essential for the development of the sophisticated experimental techniques which are vital to success in certain fields of advanced research, notably in the structure of matter and in radio-astronomy. Furthermore, the rapidly increasing use of computers will encourage the cross-fertilization of many skills in fundamentally new developments such as the study of cybernetics, as well as liberating the whole scientific and technical community from a multitude of time-consuming mental chores, and providing more scope for initiative and for inventive thinking.

It is perhaps through such team-work that the best conditions are created for a balanced interaction between science and various branches of technology, always provided that organizational structure is also geared to this objective, and that management is sufficiently enlightened to appreciate the importance of encouraging a symmetrical relationship between science and engineering in achieving a high quality of contribution to further knowledge. However, situations in which people of different specialist training are able to work together in a healthy jumble of practices are still rare, and the vast majority of scientists and engineers are destined to spend most of their working lives in the relative isolation of laboratories, universities, design offices, production sites, etc.

Here again, the problem is basically one of the practical means of communication, but like most men dedicated to a profession, the first concern of scientists and engineers will be to do a specific job to the best of their ability. It would be unfair and unrealistic to expect people with primarily sectarian interests to take the initiative in establishing the necessarily complex means of communication, and in formulating the broad lines of policy designed for a general *rapprochement* in the different sectors of the scientific and technical community. Surely the responsibility here lies with management, which is uniquely placed to take the horizontal view, and which is becoming of increasing importance with the present high degree of organization in science and in science-based industries, particularly with the general tendency away from individual research and development effort to co-ordinated teamwork.

Nevertheless, managers themselves are not always exempt from the sin of narrowness of interest, although awareness is half the battle—the most comfortable half! The already growing interest in the relatively new science of management is an encouraging sign, as supplementary training of this kind is bound to enlarge the field of interest and sympathy between individuals charged with different fields of responsibility, and may help also to achieve a more rational distribution of skills and aptitudes.

In spite of the financial and practical difficulties, the principle of 'sabbatical' leave might be applied more generously and more generally to encourage individual incentive and capacity to go on learning, and to promote a general realization of the need for education to be a continuing process throughout the life of the individual. The inconvenience and temporary loss of manpower would surely be more than compensated by the general stimulus which would result from the successful coaxing of management into a professional approach to its responsibilities, and the possibility for specialists at all executive levels to bring themselves up-to-date in their own fields, and to realize where current advancements in knowledge have produced scientific and technological 'fall-out' in allied fields of activity. The value of this kind of movement of personnel between industry, universities and research establishments has already been demonstrated on a modest scale, and there is now not only a justification, but an urgent need to enlarge the practice both within and between national boundaries.

Furthermore, the successes of C.E.R.N. in the field of fundamental research in the structure of matter, of E.N.E.A., Euratom and the I.A.E.A. in nuclear science and technology, of E.S.R.O. and E.L.D.O. in space research and engineering, and of the F.A.O. and W.H.O. in the support and conservation of human life have all demonstrated the scientific and technical, as well as the political value of international co-operation, and such organizations deserve every future encouragement as a means towards the objective of greater unity in science.

None-the-less, both national survival and the stimulus for technical advancement depend upon competitive trading, and it is therefore inevitable that commercial secrecy should present certain obstacles to a free flow of information in industrial circles. It would be quite impossible to quantify the resultant losses represented by patents, secret design information and closely guarded manufacturing techniques in terms of impediments to scientific and industrial progress, or of the inefficiency engendered under the cloak of such commercial secrecy. This will only become apparent in retrospect when each sector of industry has been able to determine what is to be gained by less restrictive policies on the flow of knowledge and information, and whereas industrial federations have done much to promote co-operative progress, the further encouragement to share industrial skills and resources must rely upon Government initiative on a national scale, and within the framework of international economic community groupings.

Government can also play an important role in sponsoring the closest contact between national scientific research programmes and industrial development work, in view of the significance of national expenditure in the overall pattern of the alliance between scientific and technological development.

It is an unfortunate fact that in the public mind, and particularly since the advent of nuclear energy, the men and women in the ranks of scientific and technical community still tend to be regarded as something apart from the run of ordinary mortals, even though as individuals they share the disadvantages of being at the mercy of their personal prejudices and quirks of temperament as all human beings. Nevertheless, the dispassionate objectivity of the scientific outlook, and the eventual readiness—in the face of undeniable evidence—to admit the possibility of being wrong, rouses strong (even if inarticulate) emotions of hostility amongst those who are devoted to the perpetuation of fantasy, and who respond by equating science with inhumanity. There is nevertheless ample evidence that the scientific community is becoming increasingly conscious of its responsibilities to society and is more competent to play a leading role in human affairs than is generally accepted. Many scientists and engineers have also come to realize that the source of ideas has become of secondary importance to both the timing of and the influence behind the expression of these ideas; they are now more prepared to compete for positions in which their professional activities are subordinated to their political functions.

A great deal still remains to be done to improve the public image of science and to remove public suspicion of the morality of scientific pursuit, and there is still scope for further exploitation of all the powerful media now at our disposal to stimulate frequent and persistent public argument and informed discussion of the issues affecting the relationship of scientists and engineers with each other, and with society at large, including very frank analysis of the human motivations which impede improvements in relations.

* * *

So much for short-term solutions in counteracting the consequences of our self-created problems. There still remains a fundamentally important influence in the evolution of thinking habits which, in the longer term, presents a much greater problem for the future integration of science and technology into contemporary culture, namely that battered but relatively unbent blunt instrument of social betterment—Education.

There is no doubt that, nowadays, many young people in the later stages of their basic education, when faced with the seemingly irrevocable choice of a life vocation, are still puzzling over the fundamental problem as to whether education is the key to a way of life or the means of earning a livelihood. Students and the public in general are continually being reminded of an apparently insatiable demand for more and more scientists and technologists, to continue the economic growth rates which have become the principal objective of all governments.

On the other hand, relatively little is known either about the degree of efficiency with which the specialized training of scientific and technical personnel is already employed in a great diversity of organizational structures, or to what extent such specialized training is essential prior to a specific professional activity. But when, in spite of possibly unfavourable social prospects, and faced with the exigencies of getting a job, the would-be scientist or engineer embarks upon his training, he is so overwhelmed by the potential scale of his studies, and by the vast accumulation of knowledge to be acquired in depth, that, not unnaturally, he seeks refuge in the specialization for which he has shown the greatest aptitude under the restricted conditions of his earlier formation. Not having been equipped, therefore, to view the whole scope of science in broad perspective, his patterns of thinking thus develop an early rigidity to the everlasting detriment of his future capacity to appreciate the problems in other fields of learning.

We have arrived then at the paradoxical situation where, collectively, man knows more now about himself and his environment than ever before in history, but is incapable of providing himself individually with more than a fragmented appraisal of this accumulated knowledge, before plunging into the relative mental security of a particular pattern of specialist thinking.

Recent history shows us that educational reform has been a continuous process throughout more than a century, at a rate which has been more or less in correspondence with social and economic evolution. However, today our experience of the rapid changes in civilized society in the last few decades, and our consequent ability to forecast the trends of the future, should provide us with an unprecedented opportunity to anticipate the kind of educational pattern which will be needed in the future, and the nature of the reforms which must therefore be put in hand today. Once again, fundamental rethinking is required, beginning with a thoroughly objective reappraisal of the relevance of the present content of education and teaching methods to the needs of contemporary society, and a critical analysis of the basic criteria in education which should be afforded to everyone, even though this might involve the relegation of some sacred pillars of learning which have masqueraded for years under the guise of logic and memory training media.

The disruption caused by radical changes need not be enormous and could be introduced in such a way as to take due account of the inertia of the present educational machinery. A golden opportunity now exists in Britain, where the ground has already been broken by the establishment of the comprehensive schools. Governmental initiative would, of course, be vital and could take the form of sponsorship of experiments in a number of provincial centres in which a specially designed course of secondary education would be dovetailed into a special degree course at selected institutes of further education. The aim should be to direct secondary and tertiary studies away from a strict sub-division into what appear to be relatively isolated subjects, and to place particular emphasis upon the evolution of ideas over the history of civilization, and an understanding of the factors which controlled the success of these ideas in their contemporary settings. Progressively detailed and lively instruction in the history of natural philosophy and religion, and their relation to the evolution of scientific thought would place the notion of entirely separate cultures in a position of total irrelevance to a unified concept of cultural activity. The historical development of mathematical philosophy, technique and application (including ultimately the elements of logic as embodied in computer theory), would then fit into these studies as part of a natural sequence. The special secondary course should also include English and at least one other language (taught by the most up-to-date language laboratory techniques), with particular emphasis on those aspects of language which limit the communication of ideas between people of different nationalities. Furthermore, a study of the fundamentals of physiology and psychology would reveal the significance of self-knowledge and encourage an awareness of human physical and intellectual limitations. An equally essential tributary to this main stream of thought would be a study of historical influences on the development of art, music and literature, and in order to gain some insight into the problems of modern Western society, the elements of economics should complete the list.

Such a special secondary course should give first priority to a philosophical treatment of the whole range of the syllabus, technological aspects being introduced as consequential and sequential, and left for further development in the tertiary course which would make provision for the study of one or two subjects in depth in addition to the continuation of the broad basic programme previously outlined. Each student would thus be provided with an opportunity of acquiring a personal concept of the full scope of the intelligence of civilized man over the centuries, and be far better equipped to form a balanced view of the contemporary scene, and for the difficult task of choosing the subsequent fields of personal preference in his further education.

Such a programme will seem over-ambitious and hopelessly impractical if judged by present concepts of what is vital and what is useful for an educated person to know. Even if the optimum solution could be found, it seems inevitable that the completion of some kind of specialized study course would have to be subordinated to the programme requirements of the individual's basic education, thus adding one or two years to the present time-scale of formal schooling. But given the resources, is this such a great sacrifice in the long term in order to achieve a society which has a greater consciousness of its scope, and a more balanced perspective of specialist activity and its contribution to human progress?

The idea is far from being new. Plato said the following in his *Republic* about the students of his Academy:

> 'They will be offered all at one time the sciences which they have studied at random in their adolescence, so that they can get a broader view of the relationships between these sciences and by this means become acquainted with the true nature of reality.'

In the fourth century B.C. it was, of course, possible to read the output of practically all the contemporary thinkers—a task which is beyond human capability today. None-the-less, it would be ironic if more than twenty-three centuries later, man has become so overwhelmed by the revelations of his own intellectual industry that he finally becomes the slave, rather than the master, of knowledge.

REFERENCES

1. HOAGLAND, HUDSON. Science and the New Humanism. *Science*, 10 January 1964.
2. WELBOURN, D. B. University Courses—A Suitable Education for the Modern World? *Journal of the Institution of Electrical Engineers*, February 1964.
3. COTGROVE & BOX. Scientists and Employers. *New Scientist*, 7 May 1964.
4. TOULMIN, STEPHEN & GOODFIELD, JUNE. *The Fabric of the Heavens*. Hutchinson.
5. TOULMIN, STEPHEN & GOODFIELD, JUNE. *The Architecture of Matter*. Hutchinson.
6. TOULMIN, STEPHEN. *Foresight and Understanding*. Hutchinson.
7. LASSERRE, FRANÇOIS. *The Birth of Mathematics in the Age of Plato*. Hutchinson.
8. SNOW, SIR CHARLES. *The Two Cultures and the Scientific Revolution*. Rede Lecture, 1959.
9. LEAVIS, F. R. *Two Cultures? The Significance of C. P. Snow*. Richmond Lecture, 1962.
10. YUDKIN, MICHAEL. *Essay on Sir Charles Snow's Rede Lecture*. Chatto & Windus.

4

JACK BELCK

Society's Segregation of Science

We are all aware of the barricades and divisions between the technologies. We realize that knowledge and understanding in one area seldom coincide with knowledge and understanding in another, and we have a vague, seldom-pursued idea that something should be done about this problem.

We blame the complexity of specialized vocabularies, the narrowness of much research, the restriction of inquiry and exposure for reasons of industrial and national security, and we recognize that today's technologist seems to have barely enough time to keep up with his own field, let alone someone else's. So we say, why not improve 'communications'?

Communications does contribute to the problem, it does serve to erect barriers between one speciality and another, but our technological tongue-tiedness is an effect, not a cause. We must dig deeper for an answer.

There is really only one serious and fundamental deterrent to a firm common ground between the technologies, and this deterrent is the product of almost universally misleading education.

Our educational systems have consistently failed to provide that form of exposure to knowledge necessary for a proper perspective of man, his past, and his present environment. Let us look at this failure.

Technology—the application of scientific knowledge to man's problems—has inevitably been treated as an entity unto itself, with no serious or considered effort to make it an integral part of human experience instead of a mere adjunct.

In other words, the arbitrary and often harmful distinction between Science and the Humanities (or Liberal Arts) has had its effect on our view of technology, and while science, pure science, can fairly well withstand this division, technologies cannot, for they are, and almost always have been, part and parcel of daily human existence.

This is our problem: we take children and put them into school where they acquire the usual basic skills, plus some history, geography and the like. They learn something of man as he was and is in his physical environment, but what they do not learn, or learn very little of, is man's use and control of this environment. In short, man's technologies are largely ignored.

Think, if you will, of the typical child's history book. Despite the fact that technology has had a profound effect on humanity, what fruits of technology find their way into print?

The Wheel
Bronze
Iron
Gunpowder
The Steam Engine
The Spinning Jenny, and a very few other artifacts.

Each item in the short list above is clearly identified as having had a profound effect on man's destiny, but none is usually identified beyond this. What is the principle behind the wheel? What is bronze? What is iron? How do we make these things? What are the constituents of gunpowder, and why will they propel a cannon-ball?

No answers are forthcoming, for the children are reading *history* books, and technology doesn't belong in a history course. It belongs somewhere else. The somewhere else will come later—separately and much later.

The many aspects and facets of science, both theoretical and applied, could be introduced gradually during the early school years, coupled to the periods in history when they actually occurred. Technology would gain a meaningful relevance if woven into the fabric of mankind's adventures.

But we make short shrift of these things in our lower schools. This is a critical omission, for an essential part of history is our conquest of what lies around us, and the 'why' and 'how' of this conquest is as important as the 'that'. Technologies, or the lack of them, have wiped out civilizations and helped create new ones, shifting centres of power not only from country to country but from continent to continent. Before too long, technology will be the force behind an interplanetary shift in power.

Parenthetically, as we skip over technology in its frame of historical reference, we obscure the fact that some of our most glorious sciences sprang from the technological empiricism of ancient times, a vital point. From among the more important technological arts, let us look briefly at shipbuilding, iron-works, and ordnance. These three were—as they are today—interdependent, with each modifying and improving the other.

Without iron, there could have been no powerful weapons to arm the ships that won new lands and resources for the conquerors. Iron-works, nudged by its own creation, the cannon, changed the ship from wood to metal which, in turn, forced still other changes and weapons.

Amusingly, while the battle of copper-bottom versus iron-clad is over 100 years past, weapons designers are still giving grey hairs to, and getting grey hairs from, their counterparts working on armourplate, while still other experts are expected to develop, concurrently, an impenetrable shield and a missile that will pierce it.

So here is our common ground, the interaction, even rivalry, between technologies that do not always prove mutually beneficial to all specialities, but which, in the long run, are almost invariably beneficial to man in general.

But our lower schools—and many of the higher ones—have ignored all this, preferring to deal with ideas rather than things, although things have been, and are, the expression of ideas, ideas formulated and systematized into a science then applied to produce things.

This disservice to technology (and to the truth) is an all-pervasive flaw, for each generation hands its own shortsightedness on to the next. We pass fleetingly over the Euclids, Archimedes, and Newtons to concentrate on speech-makers, weak-minded kings and generals who were only following orders. Worse yet, we take vital scientific minds out of their historical contexts, where they belong for at least part of the time, and assign them to later and much more specialized, dehumanized study.

Technology has been essential to mankind's progress since before recorded history, yet we bury it behind such vague labels as 'manufacturing' and 'mercantilism'. We teach the schoolboy the names of religious heretics and neglect the technology of the printing-press that made heresy the power it was.

This lop-sided, expurgated view passes for history in the eyes of our educators and those they teach. Some unnamed conspiracy sees to it that any fact which smacks of science or introduces a subject belonging to a teacher in another room is carefully weeded out.

Then, after this censorship, after having been shielded from any formal knowledge of things, the young are ushered into the presence of Science with a capital 'S'.

But science, being made up of principles, is an abstraction until it is applied, as much an abstraction as such taught-to-tedium terms as democracy, freedom and capitalism. And when the application of science is finally brought out into the light, it is hamstrung by compartmentalization, compression and dehumanization. It has to be, for no area of scientific inquiry these days can be thoroughly explored without this division, compression and dehumanization.

During the early school years, generalities and a sweeping view of science applied to the needs of men could have been taught, but now it is often too late. With lower schooling behind him, the student finds himself in an academic world where specialization and its attendant impersonal complexity is a must.

And this is why the suggestion that we can solve the problem of technological barriers by improving 'communications' is so glib. Adequate communications presupposes not only a common vocabulary but also a common understanding and appreciation; but these are just the elements lacking in our non-communicating technologists.

Except for an occasional one who is properly self-taught, our technologists feel there are barriers and obstacles between them primarily because they have never learned the significance and nature of all technologies in relation to each other. They lack awareness more than they lack vocabulary. Technologies are separate in their minds because no one ever integrated them during their school-days; no one related technologies to man.

Another point overlooked by the 'let's improve communications' school is that any given body of knowledge is an accumulation—often a leisurely accumulation—of knowledge over generations, if not centuries. But our technologists, not really raised with their subjects, are required to absorb, not a progressive, integrated experience but a vast accumulation of classified and ordered facts which are not meaningfully or obviously related to life.

This lack of connexion is sheer folly, for what, after all, is the common ground of all technologies if not to affect man's condition? And if we do not know, if we are not taught from childhood, how technologies have affected this condition, what common ground can we hope to find when we are immersed in our own specialities?

To compound the problem, those who pass through our educational systems and do not become scientists or technologists are also affected by education's misrepresentations and omissions, but the results of this are not well understood. Lord Brain, former president of the B.A.A.S., recently told an American audience that much of the popular suspicion of science rested on the failure of scientists to concern themselves with individuals and human problems.

This observation is correct, if we think in terms of scientists who work on missiles, nuclear weapons and gadgets, but, in the light of what was said earlier about the arbitrary division between science and humanity presented to this suspicious public, the blame for this suspicion must fall more on the public than on the scientists.

The public is suspicious because it, too, has failed to learn, has not been given the chance to learn, of the common ground between man and science. This has led to a complete misunderstanding of the role of science in our lives, for the direction which scientists and technologists take is a reaction to the expressed or implied needs, wants and ambitions of non-scientists.

It is easy to blame science for concentrating too much on weapons of war and gadgets at the expense of 'important' human needs, but who exactly directs the ways of science? Weapons are designed not because of some deep-seated urge in technologists to design things that kill but because malfunctioning political and social organisms require these weapons, and it is the scientist who is called upon to develop these things. Gadgets are not being shoved down the craws of humanity, humanity demands them, and once again we have an interaction between man and science that is only dimly conceived.

In the so-called social sciences, for example, we see that, while they deal almost exclusively with individual and human problems, their technologies are severely restricted. Even when some firm conclusions are reached in a social science, when there is enough information with which to build a technology such as improvement of our penal systems or mental institutions, we see that the very same public which complains of science's non-humanitarianism stands in the way of progress by standing in the way of the specialists trying to help it.

Simply stated, the vast majority of today's scientists and technologists are on *public* payrolls or in enterprises that must cater to the public in order to survive. What determines the direction and emphasis of research, then, is not some amoral or asocial scientific bent, but the demands of the market-place.

If 'too little' is being done in medical research, or 'too much' in space technology, who are we to blame if not that anonymous agglomeration called humanity? Science and technology reflect the nature and quality of the society in which they exist; like the politicians we elect to serve us, the nature and quality of our technologists are effects, not causes.

If we bear in mind that all of us are members of different publics, it becomes obvious that the suspicion mentioned by Lord Brain not only affects the non-specialist looking at the scientist but also the specialist in one area looking at someone in any other area. We have, then, an inter-technological barrier based on misunderstanding fostered by education.

Another important obstacle, and one that a refurbished educational system would largely overcome, is language. If taught properly and in a socially integrated fashion from the beginning school years, each scientific discipline and technology would probably be presented in the same language—English. Our native tongue is the richest, fullest and most precisely expressive language on earth, and yet, if we are to judge from the proliferation of scientific jargon, it would appear totally unsuited to the needs of today. This is patently untrue, as anyone who has to translate this jargon into recognizable and understandable English knows.

Because too many men in science have never had language as a living part of their scientific experience, they tend to invent words within their own disciplines and filch others from specialities not their own. Clarity and precision do not automatically result from these procedures, and the beginner who has to memorize these terms has a worse time of it than the specialist who lives with them or the non-specialist who reads translations.

Those who have mastered the language see readily that most jargon results from the inability to extract from English's vast storehouse of words and expressions the exact terms desired. Since any language is a representation of the sum total of a nation or a culture's experience, this linguistic shortcoming is evidence of a distinctly self-induced separation between the technologist and his society.

To overcome his tongue-tiedness, the specialist has allowed a new semi-science to become interposed between him and his audience: 'Communications'. Unheard of a few years ago, communications has already entrenched itself firmly in our society, and is buttressing itself not only with advanced degrees and much research but also with a jargon of its own.

Communications as a discipline was created primarily because the scientific specialist has become so narrowly specialized that he is apparently unable to express himself meaningfully to those in his own discipline and those outside it. The communications specialists have blossomed out as middlemen between speaker and audience, and the results may not be what we hope for.

The problem here is that communications as a speciality is distorted and debilitated by the same forces working against the sciences: over-specialization and dehumanization, coupled to a lack of linguistic understanding.

As strange as it may seem, articles by communications people with doctoral degrees usually have to undergo the same de-jargoning and clarification process as the most abstruse scientific/technical writing.

Tangled up in a burgeoning jargon that lifts such terms as 'positive and negative feedback loops' from older specialities, instead of using English and saying 'good and poor response', communications is becoming as over-statisticated and unwieldly as any area it is a parasite on.

We cannot solve our communications problems by turning them over to interpreters of dubious merit, nor can we rely solely on science writers and editors to clarify and translate scientific thoughts and discoveries. These last experts often can help, but usually only when acting as intermediaries between a speciality and a non-specialized public.

Within each speciality, within our scientific and technical journals and books, no such clarification is evident. It might be well, therefore, to consider some form of intra- and interdisciplinary editing. If no specialist were able to speak or to write for his colleagues, experts in other fields, or for the general public, without his message first passing through a humanizing process by an expert in the language, we could at least help to make the language barrier between technologies less formidable.

In the long run, however, we must force communication back on the scientist himself, and this we can do only by adapting our educational systems to the demands we have a right to impose on them.

But these cures take time.

Since the interaction of technologies today is far too complex to allow the random, almost whimsical, interplay of former times, we must do what we can now, with grown men, to reduce our intertechnological barriers as much as possible, but our main emphasis must be to overhaul educational systems that remain far out of step with reality.

Possibly the quickest, surest way for making up for some of education's sins of omission would be to sponsor more special intertechnical projects, as we are doing in the Antarctic, to establish viable communities in difficult or hostile environments. This project system at least forces participants to see how their own specialities integrate with others in a practical frame of reference, and if conducted, as none are now, on a very pragmatic, limited-fund basis, might well result in worth-while discoveries and material benefits.

Field-crossing magazines, lectures and organizations such as the British Association for the Advancement of Science also have their place, but truly useful knowledge and understanding of the other man's technology must come naturally, through constant, gradual exposure throughout the lifelong learning process.

This will not be easy to bring about, but the mere process of trying to reform our ways of teaching the young and informing the adult will give new insight and appreciation to those who work largely ignorant of what lies beyond their own immediate interests. When technologists are scientists first, and scientists are humanists first, the intertechnological barriers we are faced with today will largely disappear.

The 'People' (which means 'us' and not 'them') may never be fully aware of the change, but they will nevertheless benefit from it.

5

CARL HANSON

Education and the Interaction of Technologies

In the period since the second world war, during which Britain's economy has passed through many vicissitudes, the chemical industry has continually been in the van of development. It is now the second largest industry in the country and can boast an annual increase in productivity almost twice the national average. Yet, behind the success story lies a threat to the continued prosperity of this section of the economy, a threat arising from an absence of interaction between two groups of technologists. This is the conclusion reached in a recent official inquiry into the development of new chemical processes. Only one major process developed in this period was credited to British scientists. Many of the new plants now in operation employ, under licence, processes discovered in other countries. This is a patently unhealthy situation. Our chemical industry cannot hope to remain competitive in foreign markets when it is based upon second-hand processes. To obtain a lead over its competitors, it must exploit new processes of its own development. This is fully appreciated by its leaders, who have spent millions of pounds on research into new processes over the last two decades, all to no avail. Their lack of success is now officially ascribed to a lack of interaction between chemists and chemical engineers, a lack which is traced, in turn, to our educational system.

The case of the chemical industry is just one example of the ills which can arise from insufficient interaction between technologists. We are prone to such a situation in Great Britain through our determination to keep technologists in rigid compartments. This is a peculiarly Anglo-Saxon trait which is mirrored by our distinction between scientists and technologists. The former, by common accord, enjoy the higher prestige and intellectual status. Yet it is only through the technologist that the scientist can have any impact on industry, and it is only by this application of his knowledge in industry that he can benefit society. This must surely be his ideal, but it is a goal which can only be reached with the aid of the technologist. The chemist can only benefit society when his discoveries are exploited on a technical scale through the skill of the chemical engineer. The two are complementary, links of equal importance in the whole chain. In the same way, we find that the different facets of technology are of equal importance but that none are able to realize their full potential without the co-operation of the others. In such a situation it is suicidal to maintain a policy of rigid isolation.

The origins of technology are as old as man himself. It was practised by the ancients to provide the needs of life long before they were able to turn their minds to the investigation of their surroundings, which was to develop into natural philosophy and see the birth of science. Technology, however, did not progress to any appreciable extent throughout the Middle Ages. Manufacture was essentially based upon cottage industries and relied upon the skill of the craftsman rather than upon his technical knowledge. Such technological advances as were made were in the military sphere. Science, however, continued to develop and became firmly established in the centres of learning of the times. This does not mean to say that science and technology had no links. On the contrary, scientists showed a keen interest in the problems of society and often worked for their solution upon technological subjects. No, the real situation was that the scientists performed the roles of both scientist and technologist as we understand them today. There were no true technologists. Industry depended only upon technicians. The picture was suddenly transformed at the end of the eighteenth century by the Industrial Revolution. James Watt, in making possible the efficient generation of power from steam, precipitated a period which changed the whole way of life of the British people and wrought permanent change upon the landscape. The demand for machines and power brought about a technological boom. The period was to see some of the greatest figures in British engineering, men like Brunel and the Stephensons. Such men were very different in background and outlook from the scientists of the day. They were driven by commercial rather than intellectual motives. This is the period, I feel, in which science and technology began to diverge. Science was an accepted intellectual pursuit—Technology was not. Science figured at the universities—Technology did not.

Against this background, we find technologists with like interests grouping together to form their professional institutions. These, in concentrating opinion, helped more than any other factor to develop the various branches of engineering during the second half of the nineteenth century. The Great Exhibition of 1851 focused the attention of the country on its industrial achievements and helped promote a demand for educational facilities covering these technologies. From this time arose the now traditional association of South Kensington with technical education. The following years saw the development of the City and Guilds Institute of London, and the establishment of mechanics institutes in the majority of industrial centres. The latter arose largely through a demand from the technicians of the time for a greater knowledge of the machines with which they were working. From them developed our technical colleges and, in some cases, our provincial universities. Internally, these colleges and institutes were usually divided for administrative purposes into the sections of technology represented by the professional institutions. This movement was strengthened by the fact that these professional institutions were usually responsible for the final awards to be gained and consequently had a strong hold over the scheme of training adopted. Thus, whilst the professional institutions did much to foster educational development and the progress of their disciplines, they were also responsible to a large degree for the establishment of rigid compartments for each branch of engineering. Thus technologists were split within by their strivings after professional recognition for each particular discipline. Meanwhile, the whole of technology was split from science by its mode of development. Much the same situation appertains today. University courses in engineering, whilst leading to the award of a degree, are usually framed in content so as to satisfy the requirements of the appropriate professional body. University scientists still often dismiss their technological colleagues as being of lesser standing, concerned with matters of commerce rather than of true intellect.

The picture on the continent of Europe is vastly different. Vienna, one of the cultural centres of the Continent, saw in 1815 the foundation of the first *technische hochschule* and, with it, the birth of an educational system. Others were to follow rapidly. Whilst initially concerned with military engineering, it was not long before civil studies began to dominate. The *technischen hochschulen* were developed in a typically thorough way by the Germans and played an important part in the rapid industrialization of that country which took place in the second half of the nineteenth century. The chemical industry again provides a pertinent example. Employing large numbers of qualified chemists and engineers, and with their boards of directors largely comprised of technically qualified men, the German chemical companies of the time rapidly exploited the discoveries being made in the universities and *technischen hochschulen* of their country. So rapid was their progress that, by the turn of the century, over 90 per cent of the world's heavy organic chemical industry was concentrated in Germany. Great Britain was to pay dearly in 1914 for the stagnation of her chemical industry which had characterized the previous fifty years. In Germany, the technologist was seen as the most important member of the industrial team. He was the person who could apply science on a technical scale for the benefit of his country. He was trained in a special institute of university standard and enjoyed a status even higher than that of the scientist. Demand for entry was so great that only the cream of the younger generation was admitted. What a contrast from Great Britain, where the chemical industry existed with hardly any technically trained personnel, where university scientists took no interest in problems of industry, where the discovery of synthetic dyestuffs could be dismissed as an interesting exercise which could be left to the Germans to develop. It has taken us a hundred years to learn the lesson that a scientist without a technologist is of no value to the community.

Complementary to the relationship of science and technology is the problem of interdisciplinary contact within either group. Here again continental practice is quite different from our own. There a student entering university is only expected to define his broad field of interest, whether it be science, engineering or architecture. At least half his time at university is then spent on a broad course of study common to the whole faculty. Only after this stage is he expected to specialize in a particular branch of the subject. This has two advantages. Firstly, he is given a broad foundation in the whole field of, say, engineering and should therefore understand the general principles involved in all the major constituent fields. Only when he is in possession of this knowledge is he expected to decide upon which field he wishes to study in depth. In this country, by contrast, a boy is expected to take this decision before even leaving school and before he has sampled any of the possibilities. Is there any wonder we find so many boys shrinking from technological subjects and choosing for their university careers the relative shelter of the pure science subjects with which they are already familiar from school? The speciality subjects taken on the continent are usually narrower than in this country and often represent the field of interest of one particular professor. They are intended to be as much an exercise of study in depth as for the detailed knowledge gained. The development of the method of approach is considered more important than the assimilation of a large volume of factual information. The different attitude is exemplified by the final award. In Europe one qualifies as an 'Engineer'. This is the important thing; not the particular branch chosen for specialist study.

Having examined the origins of the present, strictly disciplinary pattern in Great Britain, and seen the contrast with continental practice, we are in a better position to suggest possible remedies. In terms of current Anglo-Saxon vocabulary, there are really two aspects to the problem. The first is the general relationship between scientists and technologists; the second is the promotion of interaction between the disciplines which comprise either group. The first is generally recognized, the existence of the second has only recently been appreciated.

British scientists have always been in the forefront of developments in their subjects and have been responsible for many of the world's major advances. Yet very little of this work has been of benefit to the nation. The case of synthetic dyestuffs has already been cited. Computers provide an example from the present century. The reason for this has been the lack of technologists of equal calibre to the scientists to exploit the work on a technical scale, coupled with the lack of industrial management having an interest in scientific developments. This is now generally recognized and some preliminary steps have been taken to remedy the situation. Educational facilities for technological subjects have been expanded rapidly and a healthy flow of technologists is entering industry. This has changed the statistics of the situation. Unfortunately, it has not altered the attitudes prevalent in the two camps. There is still a rift between the scientist and technologist comparable to 'The Two Cultures'. This will only be ended by a realization of their complementary nature which makes one of little value without the other. This can only come with greater mutual understanding and every opportunity must be taken to foster this amongst the rising generation in our universities. The split between science and the humanities has already led to a demand for the inclusion of liberal studies in undergraduate science courses. There has even been the daring suggestion that an element of science might well be included in arts courses as a form of liberal study. Might we take this a little further and question whether some instruction in technology during courses in pure science could not be beneficial? Is it logical that the chemistry graduate should enter industry knowing nothing of the way in which his science is applied on a technical scale? I am not suggesting that a comprehensive course should be given: merely sufficient to acquaint the scientist with the field covered by the technologist and teach him something of the vocabulary involved. To leave the acquisition of this knowledge to chance experience after entering industry is hazardous.

How can interaction be facilitated between neighbouring disciplines in either science or technology? An appreciation of the role of the neighbour, as suggested above, would help prevent psychological barriers to co-operation, but opportunities could still be lost by ignorance of the neighbour's potential. The only method which could overcome this is the adoption of a system of higher education more akin to that employed on the continent. It is essential to have a wider initial knowledge so that something is known of the scope of all allied subjects. Only then is it realistic to embark upon the deep study of some specialist branch. Whilst this object might meet with general agreement, we must seek some method by which it can be implemented without increasing the length of undergraduate courses. The duration of university studies on the continent would never be accepted in this country. They are too uneconomic both for the individual and the community. If, therefore, we have to include broader instruction within the framework of the present duration of courses and still produce a graduate having the same level of specialist knowledge, we must look to a drastic change in our educational approach.

It can now be seen that most branches of engineering and physical science are based upon a relatively small number of fundamental facts and concepts. This is not always fully realized. The historical development of the different disciplines, a development still often adopted for teaching purposes, has mitigated again the recognition of common ground between the different disciplines. Thus the average student of chemical engineering is presented with a totally different picture of thermodynamics when he studies this subject under the title of chemistry from that given during mechanical engineering. Entirely different symbols and units are employed. The student is virtually taught to treat them as different subjects. Yet the fundamental principles involved are the same. If only these could be taught together as an integrated subject and then their applications in chemistry and mechanical engineering described, much confusion would be avoided and time saved. The latter could then be used in widening the students' basic knowledge.

The undergraduate system I would suggest, therefore, as more befitting the needs of the twentieth century than that at present used in the majority of our universities is based upon a course in two parts similar to the continental pattern but restricted in total length to three or four years. In the first part of the course students would receive instruction in the basic fundamental principles of science and engineering. In the second part they would be taught how these principles are applied in the practice of one primary discipline. Thus students would have a knowledge of one discipline comparable to that gained under the present system but would also have a sufficient knowledge of the fundamental principles involved in other disciplines to allow them to venture outside their own narrow boundaries.

The preliminary part of the course, probably two years in duration, might well be common to all students of a faculty, thus relieving them at the time of entry of the difficult decision as to which discipline they prefer as a speciality. This decision would be deferred until they were in possession of a reasonable amount of knowledge upon which to base their choice. In any move to institute such a course it is this preliminary section which would pose the greatest difficulties. To prepare the syllabus will require a deep knowledge of the fundamental bases of several disciplines, together with an appreciation of their relative importance. To teach such a course will need dedication. It will be no easy matter to forget one's own training with its inherently disciplinary approach to fundamental principles. To a large extent the latter are the principles of physics. They must be presented, however, in such a way that they can be used subsequently in the development of any of the great primary disciplines which are based upon them. This will not be achieved by taking a conventional physics course of the present type. Advantage must also be taken of this preliminary period to give all students a thorough grounding in mathematics.

Equipped with such a preliminary course, students would be in a position to commence a detailed study of their chosen discipline. In doing so they would not have a partisan affinity to that discipline but would be able to see its interaction with other technologies. It could be argued that it is best to maintain a broad fundamental approach throughout. On the other hand, there is no doubt the majority would wish to see these fundamentals applied in some recognized primary discipline. Secondary disciplines could be tackled subsequently at post-graduate level.

The approach outlined above would help solve the perennial problem of educationalists in seeking a balance in university courses between a fundamental approach, which is an education but gives no preparation for a career, and a purely vocational training, which provides the latter but is not an education. It would, in fact, combine both worlds.

So far we have only considered the interaction of science-based technologies. Whilst this is the conventional approach, by adopting it we have excluded the newly emergent field of management technologies. We have, in fact, been guilty of taking a narrow disciplinary view! Over the last few decades a complete range of new disciplines has emerged within the general framework of industrial administration. Often scorned in their early days by traditional industrialists, these professional management experts have formed a clique of their own. The fields have subsequently become shrouded in mystery so far as outsiders are concerned. This presents a problem quite analogous with, and equally important to, the barriers which exist between conventional technologists of different disciplines. The management expert can have no impact in isolation. He can only benefit industry and society when he works alongside the other technologists involved. Conversely, the other technologists cannot realize their full potential unless they are aware of the services available from the management expert. The need is again for mutual appreciation and understanding.

Amongst management technologies, economics figures high in the list of importance. Our whole Western civilization is based, fundamentally, upon economics. It certainly governs our industry. Only the process which is economic will survive, no matter how crude or refined the technological steps involved. In such a situation the technologist must appreciate the economic implications of his work. The engineer must be cost-conscious. Yet how many embryo technologists receive any instruction in economics during their education? Very few. To introduce economics into an engineering degree course would usually be scorned as savouring of training as against education. Is such an objection valid? Economics is accepted in university circles as a subject for specialized study. So is engineering. Why should not the two be combined? It is only then that either can realize their full potential. Here we are approaching another continental innovation which might well be adopted in this country: the *Wirtschaftsingenieur*. He has a combined training in one branch of engineering plus economics. This may be achieved with either a blended undergraduate course or by taking a specially designed postgraduate course in economics subsequent to an undergraduate training in engineering. Here again the approach can be attacked as too vocational. However, is a course automatically a poorer education, less a discipline for the mind, when it is aimed at some practical end? This has certainly not been the conclusion of German industrialists, who are only too anxious to employ these economics trained engineers. They are in far greater demand than any group of traditional engineer, presumably because they can make a greater impact.

It is important, therefore, that we should not restrict ourselves, when discussing the interaction of technologies, to the traditional science-based subjects. At all times we must avoid intellectual snobbery. This tends to concentrate attention on to purely academic subjects and hence channels people into their rigid disciplines. A study of the boundaries between disciplines and their interactions on one another can be equally rewarding, both in the pure intellectual sense and in the knowledge that it may well have an impact on industry and hence benefit society. Few industrial problems of any significance fall conveniently within the orbit of a single discipline. Conversely, most significant advances arise from an interaction between technologies.

6

R. A. COOMBE

A Technological Education

To try and discover a common basis over which the various specialist technologies can meet, it will be necessary to range far and wide over the whole spectrum, and to look especially into the training, if any, that is common to all. This will involve, in many cases, probing into those areas that some would prefer to call engineering rather than technology, or even science. Due to the very fine distinctions involved in many cases, and in an effort not to be shackled at the outset with definitions that are too rigid, the words 'technology' and 'engineering' are used throughout the text as interchangeable terms.

Also, in such a discussion, distinction must be made between the professional technologist and the technician. This paper is concerned exclusively with the former.

As the various facets of technology become more and more complex, the more specialized the practitioner must become. It must be recognized that this is inevitable if progress is to be pushed to its furthest limits. However, much of the specialization achieved today brings with it disadvantages that are not inherent in the concept of specialization itself.

The main misfortune is the lack of intercommunication that results between differing technologies, or even within one technology itself. In many cases it is this intercommunication (cross-talk) that leads to a fundamental development. We may cite, for example, the use of radioisotope techniques in industry. Here we have a set of techniques of tremendous potential, whose application is only a minute fraction of its deserts. Why should this be so? With this particular example there is the consideration that industry may be a little apprehensive of radioactivity, whatever its form. But surely the main brake on rapid development is that nuclear engineers, with the latest measurement techniques at their finger-tips, do not know what problems are waiting to be solved, and, conversely, the technologist does not realize that his problem can benefit by the application of such methods. When the two extremes do meet, in for example the measurement of ink thickness on printing-presses, the measurement of tyre or engine wear, the tracing of tagged particles in complex industrial flow systems, the results are impressive.

The above example considered a technique applicable to many fields. The argument is of more interest when considered with regard to methods of solution of specific problems. This is where the lack of cross-talk really makes itself felt—where a technologist, endeavouring to solve a problem applicable to his specialization, does not recognize its similarities to problems previously solved in other technologies. There are many examples where such cross-talk has been very beneficial, but there must also be countless cases where the similarities remain unrecognized. We may take as a comparatively recent example the work of Shannon. He recognized, in the academic study of the geometry of multi-dimensional space, similarities with communication theory that enabled him to express how much information could be carried by a specific communication channel.

It took a Shannon to recognize this, but may it not be possible to reorganize our educational practice to make such cross-talk more probable?

Reasons for lack of cross-talk

The basic reason for the lack of cross-talk is the proliferation of specialist engineering degrees. To a rough approximation this means that the common knowledge shared by technologists in different fields is at G.C.E. Advanced Level, that is, pre-university. In several courses nowadays this might be amended to first-year degree level.

This is illustrated in Table 1. In order not to make the table too unwieldy, only some of the major technologies are considered. Others can, of course, be fitted into the table. Table 1 shows on the left-hand side the main G.C.E. Advanced Level subjects. These are followed by the degree subject, and then the technology entered by the student. Obviously the paths are not rigid, but the table does illustrate the usual type of education that is followed for a specific technology. One result of this system is that every technology, entered at postgraduate level, becomes a separate entity. This gives rise to separate Institutions, whose effects, unfortunately, are more likely to raise intertechnological barriers than lower them.

Although Table 1 is grossly approximate it shows immediately why cross-talk is difficult. Neglecting for the moment the knowledge that a technologist acquires for himself outside his own specialization, it is seen that his common link, or 'feedback', is at school level. As an

Table 1. SIMPLIFIED REPRESENTATION OF THE RELATIONSHIP OF THE TECHNOLOGIES TO THE FIRST DEGREE

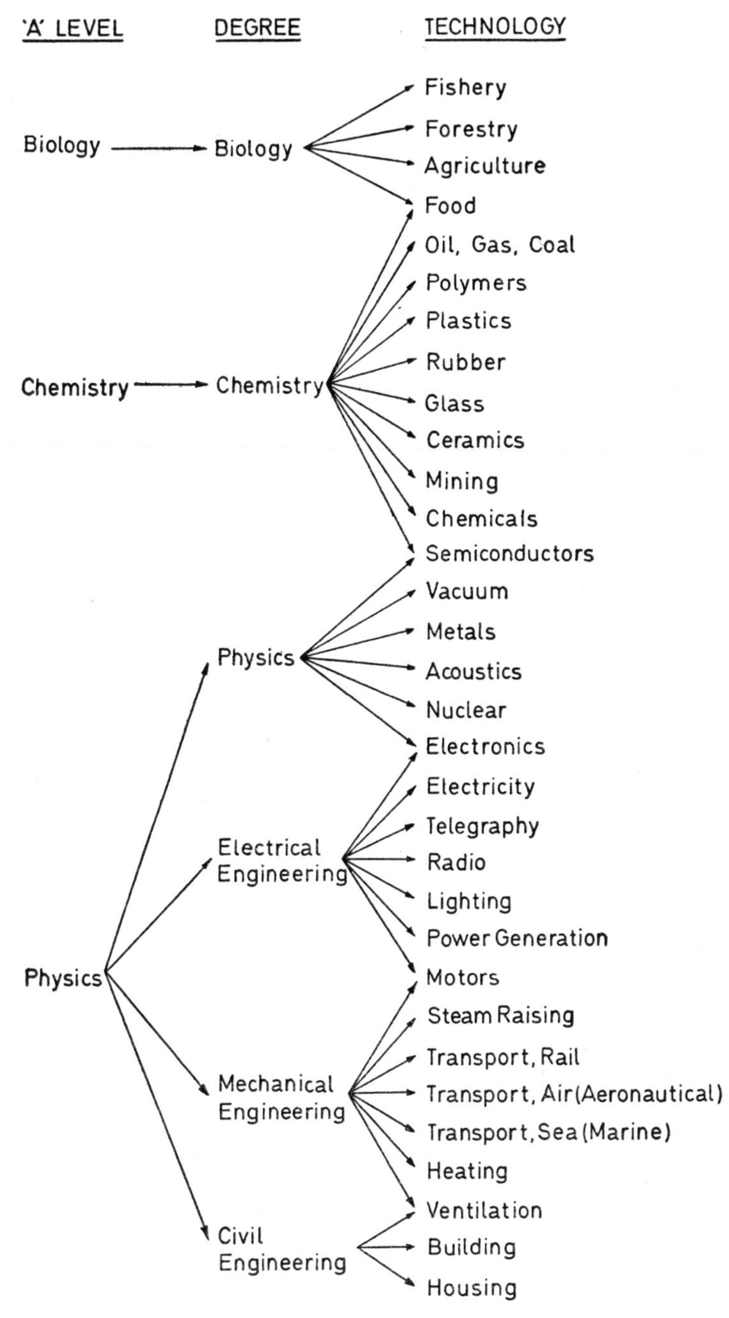

example, consider a student who takes a physics degree and then specializes in acoustic measurements. If we consider that he has never had the time or energy to read deeply outside his main course, he may have no conception of the use of his developments on transducer design to the development of radar aerials. This is because he will not have had the background of radar systems, and his feedback path with the electrical engineer has to go via school-level work, which is entirely inadequate for the purpose.

The above is only a suggested example using an assumption of a cross-talk level much lower than it would probably be in practice. Also, of course, different degree courses would cover different topics at different levels. Nevertheless, Table 1 illustrates the main ideas.

Let us note that cross-talk is not only relevant to different technologies, but also within a technology. It is only comparatively recently that semi-conductor devices have been incorporated, with great benefits, in the control systems of electrical machines. This time-lag was due in no small part to the division between the 'heavy' and 'light' current aspects of electrical engineering.

Another result of the present-day system represented in Table 1 is that when a new development takes place it can only be incorporated by developing a specific new technology. This is because basic education is not wide enough; that is, the branches of the tree diverge too early.

There are many examples of this: lasers, thin films, direct energy conversion, superconductors, materials science. Every one of these recent developments has given rise to its own technology, its own journal, and its own specialist groups.

Let us pick one, say thin films, and ask why has it given rise to a specialist technology? How does it compare with radar, for instance, which we do not consider an isolated technology in quite the same sense. Whereas thin film work involves, amongst other things, vacuum technology, solid state physics, electrical and mechanical phenomena, radar involves microwave technology, pulsed circuit techniques, aerial systems and radiation phenomena. The difference between the two is that whereas all the aspects connected with radar would be included in most electrical engineering syllabuses, the different aspects of thin film work are covered by different courses.

Thus, if it were possible for our tree's branches to diverge at a later stage, it might be possible to obviate the proliferation of further technologies.

Common basis

Table 1 shows that the great majority of technologies have a basis of physics and chemistry at the elementary stage. Might it be possible to keep this common basis to a more advanced stage? If so, would it be advantageous? An attempt to answer these two questions is now made.

Firstly, how much basic knowledge is needed by a practising technologist? Surely the more basic his knowledge the better. Only by application of fundamental principles can he progress in the true sense. This is one of the main defects of many engineering syllabuses, in that a great deal of information is presented without sufficient reference to the underlying physical principles. Let us digress again for a moment, to consider an example. Every electrical engineer knows that the conventional electrical generator design is based on the fact that when an electrical conductor is made to move in relation to an applied magnetic field, an electromotive force is produced. It is not every engineer, however, who recognizes that the principle is exactly that of the electromagnetic pump, and the magnetohydrodynamic generator. The case has become more subtle because the solid copper conductors have been replaced by other types of conductor, a liquid metal and an ionized gas respectively.

One can pinpoint the relationship of technology to basic science with reference to the game of contract bridge. For expertise in the game one must master both the art of bidding and the art of card play. It is possible to get by with facility in either technique, but the one is vastly more valuable in conjunction with the other. Are not too many technologists cutting out the bidding to their own disadvantage?

To return to the initial question, can a more common basis be sustained a stage further? Table 2 shows how this could be done, and Table 3 condenses the information. The concept can be summarized in one sentence. For the education of the professional technologist, studies of engineering should be undertaken only at the postgraduate level.

Two courses only, at undergraduate level, would suffice to train students for any of the technologies. Table 2 illustrates what might be termed the 'backbone' of the degree course. It shows the essential studies that underlie the diverse technologies. This backbone consists of the fundamental study of structure at four levels. These levels involve nuclear structure, atomic structure, molecular structure and lastly what might loosely be called lattice structure. This latter level would cover macroscopic phenomena such as viscosity, heat transfer, electrical

Table 2. DEGREE COURSE BASIC TO ALL TECHNOLOGIES

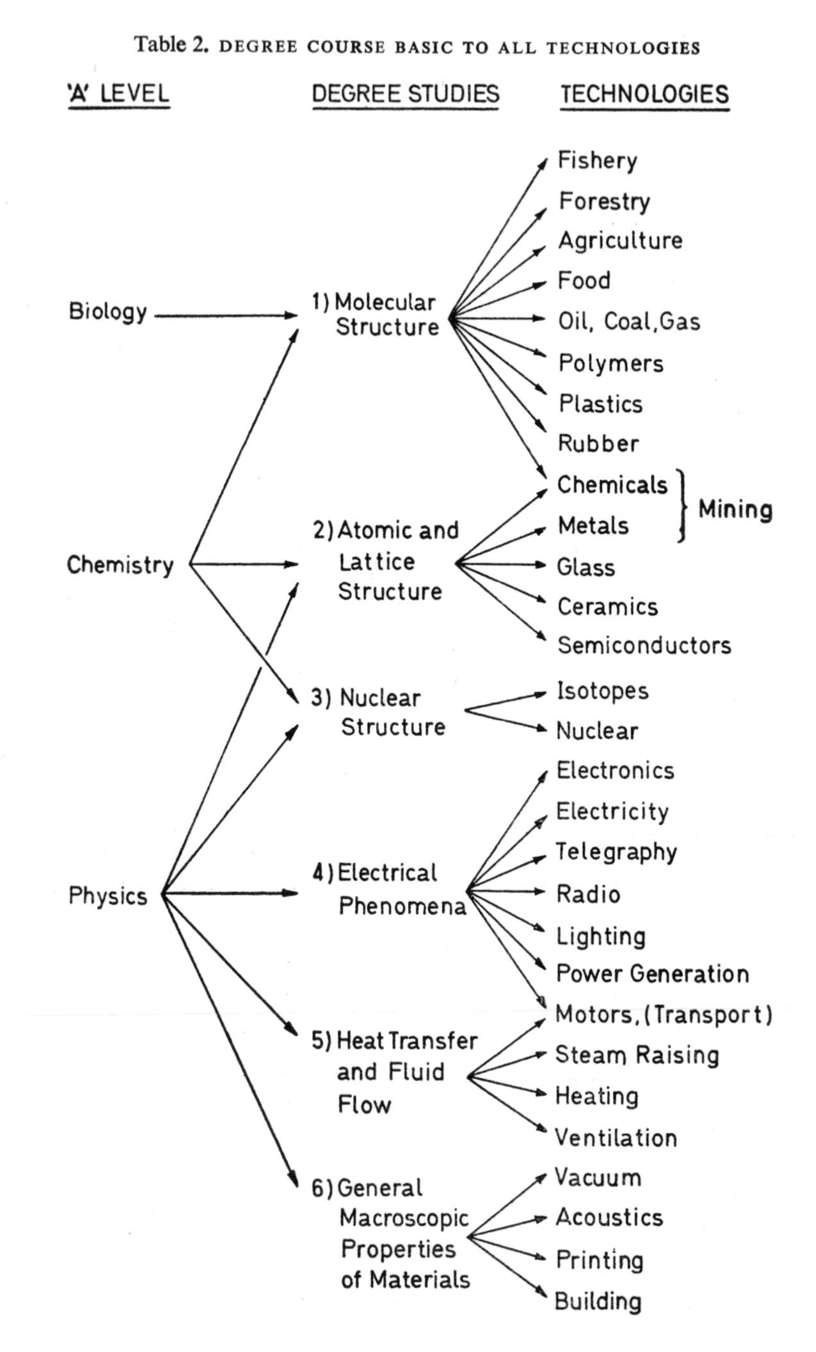

conduction, elasticity, etc. These levels are in no way meant to represent a chronological order of treatment, but simply serve to split up physical effects into convenient units. The level of the course as a whole would be appropriate to an Honours Degree.

There has been a very great interest aroused in materials technology over the past few years. Several courses are being developed, their main features begin that they are usually postgraduate, and involve the co-operation of a large number of different specialists. These range from mathematicians, through engineering scientists to various technologists, e.g. glass and plastics. In very broad terms, the course suggested above is the reversal of this, whereby the study of materials in all their aspects (structure, electrical, magnetic, thermal, general properties) forms a common basis from which the various sciences and technologies can be developed as postgraduate studies.

Any actual course would include several subsidiary subjects, not explicitly mentioned in Table 2. These would have to be picked with care, and chosen mainly with the intention of giving a background of experimental method and technique, applicable to a wide range of technologies. Measurement techniques, statistics and a basic course of electronics, as well as others, would be suitable. Also a course on physical optics, with its important ideas of interference phenomena applicable to a wide range of effects, would be valuable.

In the same way as, say, a chemistry degree from one university will differ from that of another, so the new-style B.Sc. degree would differ in content from place to place. However, it is envisaged that this difference would rest with the content of the subsidiary subjects, and that the 'backbone', discussed above, would be common to all.

Naturally, mathematics would be incorporated throughout the whole structure of the degree. Mathematics, carefully handled, can provide some most fruitful illuminations of the underlying similarities of seemingly unrelated effects. For example, the solutions of such general equations as those of Laplace or Poisson, or those describing diffusion or wave processes, can correlate widely different physical effects, leading to a much wider appreciation of physical phenomena.

Table 3 indicates that all students would take either one of two routes, depending upon their ultimate goal, though the final choice of specialization could be left until after the attainment of a first degree. It is clear that course B, Table 3, is envisaged as basically an applied physics degree. When saying 'all students', this includes those whose interests are in physics as a subject in its own right. Table 3 shows that

Table 3. CONDENSED VERSION OF TABLE TWO

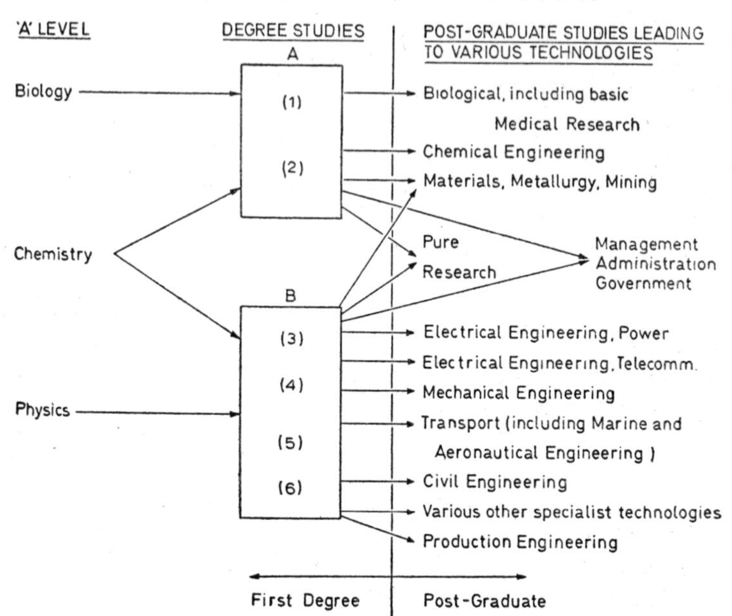

pure research is also envisaged as a postgraduate activity, taking its place as an alternative together with the whole range of technologies. The effect of this is discussed later.

Operation

To summarize the above section, all students, whatever their final objective, would take one of two basic degrees. There is no reason why this could not be entitled B.Sc.

Equipped with this basic knowledge, a student would then spend a further period studying his selected specialist technology. At the end of this period he would receive a further qualification, B.Tech.* This would apply to all students except those following pure research, who would read for a higher degree in the usual way.

It must be emphasized that it would not be necessary for all students to read for a B.Tech. A student obtaining a B.Sc. could readily find employment in industry, or elsewhere, as an applied scientist, and of course could learn his technology via industry rather than via college.

*Since writing this essay, some new universities have decided to call their first degrees B.Tech. There is no similarity between the two.

Table 4. COMPARISON OF THE STRUCTURE OF VARIOUS COURSES. THE SHADED AREA REPRESENTS THE PERIOD SPENT IN INDUSTRY

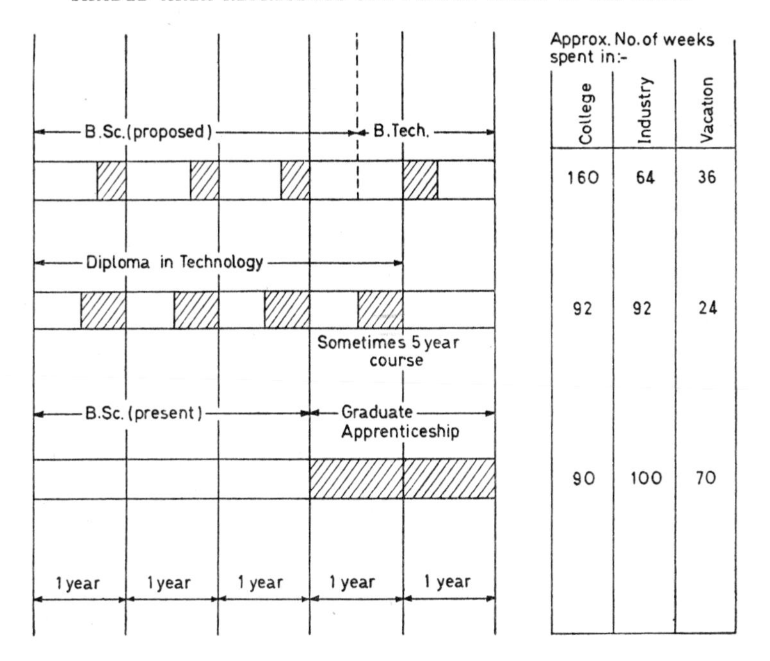

The form of B.Sc. course is envisaged as a sandwich scheme lasting three and a half years, with a further eighteen months to the B.Tech.

The structure of this scheme is illustrated by Table 4. It will be noticed that the periods in industry are shorter than the periods usually used in the present Diploma in Technology schemes (six months). The reason for this is that the aim of the periods in these two schemes is not identical. In the course envisaged in this paper, the industrial period serves to bring the student into direct contact with actual technological applications of the fundamental principles that have been studied in the college period. There is no need for all periods to be spent in the same industry. In fact it would probably be advantageous if the student could see, at first hand, the same basic principles applied in a variety of different technologies.

The scheme up to B.Tech. would take five years, and this can be compared with the alternative arrangements of first degree (three years) together with a Graduate Apprenticeship (two years), or Diploma in Technology (four years). In some colleges this latter course has been extended to four and a half or even five years. A rough comparison of the three schemes, allowing for the usual holidays, is given in the columns on the right-hand side of Table 4. It may be more illuminating to compare the B.Tech. with the five-year Diploma in Technology, with regard to the approximate number of weeks that can be allocated to the time when instruction specific to one technology is given. For example, even in the fifth year of such a scheme, mathematics, liberal studies, administrative courses, etc., usually occur, and these are not specialist technology subjects. It is estimated that over the five-year period the Diploma in Technology student receives the equivalent of forty weeks' specialist technology instruction, and the B.Tech., fifty weeks. So the latter course actually achieves more teaching of the technology, and does so on a more solid basis. Of course the Diploma in Technology student spends twice as long in industry, but this takes no account of the relative aims of the two types of industrial period.

This point is important, and bears repeating. The envisaged course is not a watered-down version of an engineering degree, but should reach as high a standard as is achieved now, but on a firmer fundamental foundation.

Discussion

Let us consider in more detail some of the general features of the course as illustrated in Tables 2 and 3.

The feedback path for cross-talk can now take place at a very much higher level. The glass technologist can now explain his development to the civil engineer by virtue of the fact that they both have the same B.Sc. degree, and can draw upon the fundamentals imparted on that course to discuss their work. This should mean that any developments in one technology would be transmitted to applications in other fields at a much greater speed than at present.

The structure of the B.Sc. should help to some extent in curbing the proliferation of technologies, as complete entities in themselves. Consider, for instance, that chelates, whiskers, or masers were to rapidly develop into a major technology. Such studies could readily be incorporated as a postgraduate study, based on the fundamental B.Sc. This would avoid the inevitable emergence of a Diploma in Whisker Technology course, recruiting students at 'A' level (with attendant difficulties), and producing very narrow-track specialists. The proliferation of Diploma of Technology, and degree courses, pandering to very specialist followings, which are becoming more common today, cannot be a good innovation.

There are two more advantages that, although not directly related to the problems of technological diversification, are worth a mention. First, a B.Sc. degree would provide a very worth-while education in its own right. We do not expect a history student to become necessarily a historian, or a graduate in Latin and Greek to find a career involving intimate knowledge of these languages, but on the whole we do expect a present-day B.Sc. to become a professional scientist. One reason for this is, of course, due to the present-day shortage of scientifically trained personnel in scientific pursuits. One hopes that in the future it will be more common than it is now, to find employees in influential governmental and industrial positions whose basic education was in the sciences. The B.Sc. (new type) would provide a very useful broad science degree for this type of education.

The other interesting, and perhaps far-reaching, effect of such a scheme is that pure science would be placed on the same footing as applied science. One of the main problems today is to overcome the barriers that divide the two activities, and also to get over to schoolmasters in particular what a technological education involves. These men are important in that to a large extent it is their influence or advice that sends a schoolboy on to a pure science course, rather than an engineering one. With one swoop it might be possible to eliminate this problem. All schoolboys would enter one of the two B.Sc. degree courses. During the period of this course, including their sorties into industrial territory, they would be able to formulate their own ideas of what technology they would like to ultimately pursue. The hour of decision could be left for a further three and a half years.

At the end of the common B.Sc. course there would then be no distinction between the various channels available. The prospect of doing postgraduate research in pure chemistry would hold no distinction over the prospect of reading postgraduate marine engineering.

The concept of one channel being more intellectually challenging than another would largely disappear, and the distinction between pure and applied science, or between pure science and development, would greatly diminish. If these boundaries did vanish then the effects throughout the country, from the Royal Society to the grammar school, could be dramatic.

Perusal of the correspondence columns of many of the various Institutions' journals shows a contemporary interest in the enhancement of the status of the engineer, and differentiation in the public mind between the technician and the professional engineer. The proposed B.Sc. course would go a long way towards meeting these objects. Firstly, with engineering a postgraduate study, everyone would have a common high-level background, and could appreciate and delineate the field of the other's endeavour. Secondly, whilst abolishing the old concept of specialist engineering degrees, it would be a trivial extra step to abolish at the same time the word 'engineering' from the professional vocabulary, if generally thought desirable. Either a different word could be synthesized or, perhaps better, the word 'technology' used in this context.

A student would then take a B.Sc. followed by a B.Tech. in, say, the Building specialization of Civil Technology, calling himself a technologist, pure and simple.

As another advantage of the scheme, consider also the fluctuating need for various types of technologist. To take a broad classification, suppose that a great need arose for mechanical engineers. It would be far simpler to endeavour to persuade non-committed students on a B.Sc. course to take up postgraduate specialization in some field of mechanical engineering than it would be to persuade increased numbers of 'A' level schoolboys to start on a mechanical engineering degree. The time-scale between demand and supply would also be considerably reduced.

It is conceivable that a technologist could be re-trained in another technology. He would have his basic B.Sc. training to fall back on, and could be re-trained from there. If three years pure research led to a doctorate, as at present, a similar award (D.Tech.) might be given to a student who satisfactorily completed two eighteen-month training periods in different technologies, after his initial B.Sc.

Concerning the teaching staff requirements, the position would be likely to improve. More teachers on the fundamental side would be required, drawn from the existing ranks of specialists (specialization is not very high at first-degree level). With a common degree course, teaching arrangements could probably make better use of lectures to very large audiences (why not 500? Timoshenko did over thirty years ago!), followed by splitting into smaller discussion groups under tutorial guidance.

The education of large numbers on common courses, which include industrial periods, would seem to lend itself very well to the 'end-on' sandwich scheme; particularly with regard to the utilization of industrial training places. However, we will not get involved in the merits, or otherwise, of the scheme here.

What are the disadvantages of the common course, outlined above? One that could possibly occur is that the teaching approach become too academic. This might result in the production of a large number of applied physicists with no real conception of the working, of the needs, of industry. It is not proposed to discuss this in detail here for one very good reason. If such a misfortune should occur, then it would be as a result of the methods of teaching employed, rather than an inherent de-merit of the scheme itself.

It might appear at first sight that because the course is broader based, it must reach a lower level. That this is not so has been shown above, the reason being that the times available are utilized in somewhat different ways.

Finally, great thought would have to be given to the form and content of the industrial periods. In particular, industry would not be likely to benefit from them to any large degree. It might be necessary for the government to subsidize a training facility that was incorporated within an industry.

New role of the Institutions

In the following discussion the word 'Institution' is used as a generic title to cover all Institutions, Associations, Groups, etc., formed with the intention of furthering a particular specialist technology.

In the main it would appear that the present arrangement of the Institutions does not lend itself easily to the lowering of intertechnological fences. The tendency is for demarcations to become even more rigid, not allowing that latest developments in any technology must embrace a multitude of different disciplines.

Consider an elementary device such as a thermocouple. The development of such an instrument to measure very high temperatures is of direct interest to many technologists, including, for example, aerodynamicists, reactor engineers and furnace technologists. Developments in such devices will involve either semi-conductors or ceramics, or both, and one of the main problems will be chemical compatibility. Also, metallurgy will feature in the manufacturing process, and probably spectroscopy in the calibration procedures. Even with this very simple example we have at least eight different technologists involved, and almost eight different Institutions.

The practising technologist, however, will probably find that his background training will only allow him to obtain membership (of any description) to one, or perhaps two, Institutions. The reason for this is that the various Institutions have evolved in an effort to satisfy two different kinds of demand, and have drawn up their entry requirements accordingly. On the one hand they wish to aid in the promotion of advanced work, and on the other they want to provide a corporate membership qualification to show competence in a particular technology. This latter function works primarily for non-graduate engineers, though the corporate membership of many Institutions is a valued higher qualification. Both the above demands are worthy of satisfaction, but unfortunately they are to some extent incompatible.

At the moment the Institutions have remedied this by setting up the Joint Council to consider the common interests of all engineers. An alternative way in which the Institutions could greatly help to promote technological exchange would be to throw open their doors to anyone holding a B.Sc. who is prepared to pay the subscription fee. This would mean that any qualified person could gain access to all symposia, journals, colloquia, etc., organized by any Institution, and could follow his interests freely, regardless of arbitrary boundaries. The corporate structure could remain intact by forbidding the use of any designation to such members.

Thus the restraining barriers would vanish with no harm done to the Institution, and the complete corporate membership structure would remain. This would still provide a useful designation of technological competence for students who left college at B.Sc. level and went straight into industry, and for students who have followed a non-university path to professionalism.

Conclusions

In looking for the common ground of the technologies the author is aware that he has looked at what can be done for the future development, rather than how existing barriers can immediately be overcome. It is recognized that the innovations required would take several years to become fully effective, and that the idea of two basic degrees might have to be incorporated with other structures, rather than being absolute. Unfortunately lack of space does not allow the manifold aspects of the scheme to be discussed further.

It has been shown that a course, involving mainly the various and diverse microscopic and macroscopic properties of materials, can form the basis from which the postgraduate studies of various technologies can emerge.

Various benefits arise from such a scheme, and these are summarized in Table 5. Not least is the hope that it may curb the proliferation of more and more undergraduate specialist courses. There are even those who would teach engineering as a school subject, a project that would surely make any existing barriers even more secure.

The idea presented here has been only the underlying theme. Several problems remain as to the form of the course and the subsidiary subjects also studied. Some indication has been given of these extensions to the basic idea; sufficient to show that it would support a structure of further education and training in any one of the many technologies. In all probability a better meeting point could be found between any two or three particular technologies, but the author contends that the solution above, with minor variations, should be applicable to all.

Table 5. ADVANTAGES OF A COMMON DEGREE COURSE WITH TECHNOLOGICAL STUDIES MADE AT THE POST-GRADUATE LEVEL. SUMMARY OF POINTS DISCUSSED IN THE TEXT.

1. Common level of knowledge is at a considerably more advanced level, leads to shorter feedback path and hence greater cross-talk.
2. A new technology is easily adapted into the basic framework, avoiding proliferation of specialized undergraduate courses.
3. Recruitment much easier, in that it takes place at post-graduate and not school level.
4. Student sees engineering science in a broad context and can leave choice of specialization until after first-degree level.
5. Easier to balance short-term demand for particular types of technologist.
6. Provides basic science degree for management trainees, government administrators, etc.
7. Pure and applied science seen as related postgraduate studies, with consequent reduction in intellectual distinctions.

7

ALEX L. MARSHALL

Technology, Society and the Specialist

Man is perpetually restless, even uneasy and discontented; constantly trying to change and improve himself and the things about him, he probes, discovers and develops what is in his environment, trying to control it to make life easier and more interesting for himself. An idealist picture, perhaps, because not every man is aware of it, nor does every man wittingly contribute, but, fundamentally, the sum of human endeavour might be so described. Modern man, the current product of this endeavour, might in fact be considered unnatural in an artificial environment, to such an extent has human effort carried us. No longer need civilized man feed, clothe and shelter himself with what he can wrest from nature with his own hands.

At least, that might be the superficial picture, but if man is a product of evolution, then what he produces must be part of the evolutionary process and civilized society might still be described as natural. However, this is perhaps to indulge in mere semantic quibbling. The intention here is not to discuss the motivation behind nor the place in the natural order of modern civilization, although without some such notion it is difficult to consider the place of any human activity.

Many things of course contribute towards the improvement of the lot of mankind. No study is completely independent of any other. Quite apart from the immediate or direct contribution of, for example, science to technology and its converse, each of these has some effect on society as a whole. As a result, how the members of society think and what they think are affected to a greater or lesser extent, since those members are influenced by their environment—society. Despite its complexity, in fact, modern society might be likened to a lake whose level will rise, however slightly, when the smallest amount of water is added, affecting everything within the lake and around its shores.

If we accept this argument, then, it is not difficult to see that there must be some degree of interaction between many, probably all, fields of study. Here, however, the intention is to consider only technology in its many forms. Without some such restriction it would be impossible to discuss the theme of interaction adequately, but more important, unless we focus our attention on a particular aspect, the argument might become so general that it loses impact. In particular, sight might be lost of the possibility of doing something to counter the dangers that many of us feel face us in the over-specialization that exists today. This will be returned to later.

* * *

All technologies contribute to and derive something from society. Since they must depend on people for their promotion, they must equally be affected by how these people think and what they know. Indeed it might be said that the only effective interaction is within the minds of men, because no development is possible without thought. Machines do not evolve by themselves, they are not self-propagating. What they do is extend the scope of man's capabilities, enabling him to achieve things beyond his own physical capacity and so improve his way of life. As a result he comes to *assume* that certain things can be done, opening the way to further extensions of ability with their consequent further assumptions of the possible, and the cycle of progress starts again. The most obvious example of this is the development of heavy cranes—some can lift 500 tons. Compare this with the lifting power of a man's arms!

With this extension of capability has come the development of many specialities, each with its own expertise because the range of knowledge required of modern man is so vast. Necessary though this may be, it is becoming a curse of civilization because too many specialists develop their own language (if that is not too dignified a word), their own techniques, their own tendency to refine and learn more and more about less and less. The words of Dean Swift are not inappropriate:

> 'So Nat'ralists observe, a Flea
> Hath smaller Fleas that on him prey.
> And these have smaller Fleas to bite 'em,
> And so proceed *ad infinitum*.'

Only now for 'Flea' we might substitute 'Specialist'.

If we use a more comfortable image, specialists might be likened to animals grazing in fenced fields, but they are often too busy cropping the grass to raise their heads and see the gaps in the fences.

Although it is possible to exaggerate the dangers that face us as a result they are nevertheless real, and it is not difficult to imagine the loss of efficiency there must be through failure to communicate adequately.

Anyone who is familiar with the power industry, for example, cannot fail to be aware of the difference in approach, in philosophy if you like, between civil and mechanical engineers. Unfortunately, too many people either do not realize the problem exists or, realizing it, feel it cannot be solved. Solve it we must, however, if we are not to waste our resources.

* * *

Demonstration of interaction is simple if we regard technology in its most general forms. In fact, we need only examine a little of the historical evidence. How much of industrial society depends on the production of steel? The evidence is all about us, but none of this would be possible without the development of the open hearth and the blast furnaces and their modification and improvement. The production of better quality steels and modern techniques of rolling and pressing have affected every feature of modern life, from cans to motor-cars, from machines to great bridges.

That improvements are not always recognized as being desirable has been epitomized by the Luddites, so that with development in techniques of technology has come the need for development in techniques of persuasion and communication. Indeed the most difficult problem facing us is not the collection of information but its distribution. This is a point that will be returned to later; it might be more useful first to attempt some sort of general classification of technologies; if only to illustrate how difficult it is in fact to segregate them—an illustration of counteraction, perhaps.

* * *

In relation to man, his environment and society, technology might be classified under four main headings. Almost all branches of technology can be classified under more than one of these headings and each, through its effect on man and society, affects the others. This is interaction in its perhaps most indirect form, but little thought is needed to demonstrate their effect.

Man must be housed, fed and clothed, he must be able to move about the earth, he must be able to communicate and he must be able to control his environment. Broadly speaking, then, technology can be divided into domestication, transportation, communications and environmental control. Brief consideration of these shows how they are interlinked, but some elaboration is perhaps desirable.

Domestication

The word is clumsy and a little misleading but in general it comprises building, food and clothing. Building rather than housing because man at work must be sheltered as well as man at play and man at rest. Many of his machines must also be housed and most industrial processes are impossible without a protective shell—not always a mere shell, in fact, but an integral part of the process.

While building is easily recognized as a technological discipline, it is not always recognized that the production of food is highly industrialized. Not just in the mechanization of farming but also, for example, in the packaging of food. Much of what we eat is packaged in metal, paper, wood or plastic, and in the use of materials are involved many different studies. Their manipulation by machines depends on their physical properties. Whether they can be pulled, twisted, bent, pressed, stamped or sealed is a function of these properties and the design of the machines that handle them is equally a similar function—indeed, it becomes, as do so many other things, a chicken-and-egg problem.

The foods that fill these packages are also the end-result of industrial processes, either in their preparation and production or in their refinement. Bread, butter and jam, even.

So it is with furniture and clothing. These two are mass-produced in the main, either in their fabrication or in the production or modification of the materials from which they are made. The evidence of this is all about us, in our homes and where we work.

Already we have mentioned two of the key features of modern technology or of an industrialized society: materials development and mass production. These are fundamental to practically every technological process; the first to enable it to be achieved and the second to allow it to be done economically. If waste of resources is to be avoided, any process must make the best use of the materials available and it must do so as cheaply as possible.

Transportation

Basically this concerns the construction of mobile containers for people, goods and materials and facilities for their movement and maintenance, whether by road, rail, sea or air. The modern car industry is founded on processes that are an extension in scale of those to be found in canning factories. The production of railway carriers, aircraft and ships is a further extension in scale to a certain extent. Hence materials development and mass-production techniques are not far removed from a further branch of technology.

In addition, a source of motive power is necessary and however this is provided it must affect the design of the vehicle it propels. Vibrations alone bring serious problems, vibrations both from the engine and the medium through or on which the vehicle moves. Problems of temperature and fatigue, inertial forces in addition to normal loading stresses: all these are vital and in their train bring many associated fields of study. Fuel is essential, whether for direct propulsion or through the medium of electricity. So it goes on—the difficulty lies in fact in confining the argument. Extend it to roads, railways, docks, harbours, airfields and its scope widens enormously.

As to the impact on society of transportation, this needs no amplification to any thinking man: he need only consider what place the motor-car is to have in the life of such a congested country as this.

Communications

Much has been said and written about the impact of mass media on the world in which we live. The communication of knowledge, information, even entertainment is vital to our future development, and its great spread is only possible through the printed or spoken word. That the improvement in communication has not always been to mankind's benefit is well enough known, but it is to be hoped that the good far outweighs the bad.

The printing-press, the radio and television are all products of technological development. The extension of their use and capabilities depend on the capacity of technologists to improve, refine and develop. Scientific discoveries may revolutionize theories but industrial application is only possible through technology, and it is in this application to communication that technology has had its greatest impact on society. It can be truly said that in this, men's minds have been affected.

Environmental control

This final subdivision governs the possibilities inherent in all the others. The development and control of natural resources is essential to the provision of ores, food, water, power. Consider power alone: electric power can be provided by water, coal, oil, gas, nuclear energy, even the wind and the sun, and all these require many types of engineer, metallurgists, fuel technologists and a host of others. Omit any one and the system ceases to function—it can in fact be likened itself to an electric circuit which must be closed before current flows. And by now it should be obvious that this analogy can be extended to all technology.

The current in this circuit is knowledge and it has to overcome many types of resistance, but how much of this resistance is necessary? Two almost contrary examples will illustrate this.

It can perhaps by now be assumed that interaction is almost self-evident and technological development in one field can revolutionize many others. The growth of the computer and electronics industry is perhaps the most spectacular example in recent years. 'Computer' is almost a magic word now and the result is we may be in danger of over-confidence in the abilities of computers: they are after all only as effective as the men who build and use them allow them to be. This, then, is a resistance to caution.

Contrast this with the machine tool industry. An industrial society is built on this industry, it is a staple of any modern community. And yet it has recently been demonstrated that, in this country at least, there has been considerable resistance to the application of electrochemical machining techniques which are capable of revolutionizing the whole of industry. Here is resistance born of over-caution.

These are perhaps extreme cases, but a passing knowledge of statistics should make us ask how many examples are there between the extremes? What waste results from sheer ignorance?

Unfortunately, as each of us progresses through life, we tend to specialize increasingly. We forget many of the things we were taught which do not immediately concern us, and, even if we do remember, what we remember may be out of date. Even more unfortunately, there are few among us who seem to realize this, or, realizing it, do anything about it. It is as if our spirit of curiosity is stifled gradually as we get older. It is a situation that is easy to condemn but also easy to understand. Any modern technology covers a great deal of ground in itself and it is difficult to keep abreast of current developments, even in one's own field. The proliferation of technical magazines and journals makes it a physical impossibility to read everything written.

Closeted knowledge is one of the greatest barriers to industrial progress—to any progress, in fact. If many of us seem unaware of interaction, how many more of us are fettered by our ignorance? Tragic ignorance, because we do not even realize we are ignorant. Progress can only be achieved efficiently by the free dissemination of knowledge. In short our problem is one of education and communication—how is this education to be achieved? How are people to learn about things they do not realize they ought to know?

If it is admitted that we need more general technological education, the problem can be regarded in two ways. Firstly, for those starting their education—the need here can be relatively easily met because where there is a virtual vacuum of knowledge it is merely a matter of adjusting the method of filling the vacuum. The methods of training for the requirements of the Atomic Energy Authority may be the widest based training system in British industry, and it is encouraging that at least one body has recognized the need for men with open minds. Although this is no doubt also true of others it is probably not true of the majority, in fact rather than in theory, and to some at least of us this is to be regretted.

Second, and the more difficult aspect of the problem, how are the many who have long passed the learning of fundamentals to be persuaded? (Persuasion is but a facet of education.) What sketchy knowledge we are likely to have beyond our immediate sphere of interest is probably out of date. Perhaps this exaggerates the difficulty, but it exists nevertheless. Many of us must often feel depressed when considering what we feel we ought to know. We have, after all, only a limited amount of time available to us and there are many things to be done in that time. Quite apart from the routine necessities of life there is enjoyment to be had and our education to be extended beyond the limits of anything merely connected with making a living. Although this is outside the scope of this paper it should not be ignored—in fact, a man with a wide variety of interests may be more prepared or more easily persuaded to consider another point of view.

We are then faced with the basic problem of so systematizing and disseminating knowledge that it is possible for us to be aware of techniques and developments outside our apparent immediate interest but which might well affect it did we but know it. In short we have to be able to know things we do not know we need to know.

* * *

One hesitates to suggest adding to the overwhelming array of magazines and journals with which we are faced but surely the most obvious answer to our problem is a technological newspaper. Not another magazine but a bulletin which is easily assimilated. Most of us manage at least to skim through our daily newspapers and gain even a passing knowledge of affairs: the ability to do so seems to be an attribute of civilized man. How simple it might be then to behave similarly with a technological newspaper. Not daily, nor even weekly: perhaps once a fortnight or month. Finance is the problem, but it is surely not insurmountable: would our learned bodies contribute? At least they might sponsor such a project. So far commonality of interest among many bodies has been recognized by the formation of, for example, the British Nuclear Energy Society and, more recently, the Engineering Institutions Joint Council, even by the appointment of Ministers of Science and Technology: it does not seem difficult to extend this a little further. Would some of our major industrial organizations be prepared to provide funds?

If the varied staff of a daily newspaper, which includes experts in many fields, can interpret political, economic, scientific, technical and artistic events in terms any literate man can understand, surely the same can be done for technology. Almost all technical journals appear to be written for the insider and most articles written by and for a variety of specialist insiders. There is therefore a barrier of knowledge and of language between them and most others. We already have in daily use the common language that is necessary, leaving us with the barrier of knowledge. This could be overcome by making available easily read, easily assimilated information. No article longer than 500 words, journalese, headlines even—popularizing undoubtedly, but it *can* be read easily, which means it takes little time and it can arouse interest and curiosity. Once this occurs, further information is not difficult to obtain.

Detailed and expert knowledge of every aspect of technology is impossible for any one man to have but it does not mean he need have a blinkered existence.

* * *

This then might bring publicity and stimulate curiosity but information acquired in such a form is done so accidentally. Desirable though it is, since many developments occur almost by accident and inspired curiosity is extremely valuable, it does not solve the problem of discovering what might be useful from elsewhere in a given situation. A systematic and logical process of thought is required—how is this to be done easily?

In the world of planners, critical path techniques are extremely useful. Complex operations are built up from many smaller and simpler operations, some of which take longer than others, some of which are linked, some of which are independent, some of which run consecutively and some concurrently and so on. All of them, however, are essential to the complete process and all of them take time. The critical path is the one which gives the combination of operations defining the minimum time in which the whole can be performed. Every other operation is interlinked with this critical path, of course, but this is the governing, the critical, sequence. What we seek are the critical paths of technology.

It is difficult to generalize but to consider a particular case presupposes the specialist knowledge we are trying to overcome. Let us then try to generalize.

A critical path programme is built up from arrow diagrams. These are simply connected lines, each of which represents one operation. They are arranged in sequence and obviously some will be dead-ends (the whole thing is rather like a diagram of railway sidings)—in preparing a programme for building a house for instance, plastering would be a 'dead-end'. No other operation depends on it although the house may still not be ready for occupation. Without describing the whole technique it would be difficult to explain this fully and the example quoted is not the best (what about decoration, for example?) but the basic idea is in fact simple enough.

Select any one subject, then, and proceed to build up its critical path diagram—or family tree. Its complexity is a function of the detail we put into it but the important thing is that it defines associated subjects, it leads to objective thinking, it opens up fields of inquiry. And this last is perhaps the most important because it widens our scope.

Any systematization is of course principally cross-referencing, however it is done. Our main object should be to stimulate curiosity. After all, the most efficient method of co-ordinating or collating information is worthless unless people can be persuaded to use it. In this lies the major obstacle to progress because every field of human inquiry depends on people, and unless people are prepared to co-operate, are interested, are willing to extend themselves, the burden for any one man becomes insupportable. Admittedly many discoveries have been made by individual workers but technology concerns fundamentally the improvement of man's condition and it is therefore a matter for the many, not just the individual.

What is needed is publicity for the idea that technologists should not confine themselves to their own disciplines, and the corollary to this is simplicity. It is pointless for the metallurgist to expound on crystallography and phase diagrams to the machine designer who merely wants to know the limits to which he can extend his use of the metal. It is pointless for the electronics engineer to expound on transistors and solid circuitry to the structural designer who merely wants to use a computer to analyse his framework. Despite this, the machine designer and the structural engineer must at least have some appreciation of the problems of the metallurgist and electronics engineer. Unless all these people realize that mutual understanding is vital, however, progress is bound to be difficult because their common ground is so restricted. It is unnecessary to explain things in terms a child would understand, but a greater use of basic English would help considerably, instead of using esoteric technical terms and definitions.

Common understanding is without doubt possible and in many cases is achieved, but how much wasted effort is there in the achievement. How much *more* understanding is possible?

It has already been suggested that critical path techniques will help in this but herein lies a danger. Systematization requires classification, and however this is done it induces concepts of boundaries and subdivisions which in fact impose upon us once more the very problem we seek to overcome. As soon as we start to classify, we imply restrictions and so tend to reduce common ground, which is the very negation of the case we seek to argue.

Hence in applying any such technique it is essential to remember that its primary purpose is to open up new fields of inquiry, not define spheres of interest. Mere classification or subdivision or cross-referencing is, after all, largely a clerical task. We should be trying rather to change our approach, our processes of thought. Too many of us are too inward-looking, introverted almost, when we should be reversing our sight-lines and looking outward. But we must be able to understand what we see and be understood: we must learn to communicate.

Our learned societies perform an invaluable function but we need a common forum. It need not be a learned body, after all; society is a forum to which we all belong. As members of it we should be able to arrive at a common understanding, if not philosophy, and to do this we must educate and be educated. That is the real problem.

Mankind depends on technology for its survival. If technologists cannot communicate how much needless waste and misery are ultimately caused by their failure to do so.

8

ALFRED M. PRINCE

The Need for Hybrid Vigour

Inbreeding provides a mechanism for assuring a stable repository of useful traits. The inbred strain, on the other hand, is generally of somewhat reduced fertility, and vigour.

High degrees of fertility and vitality are usually achieved by interbreeding of inbred strains. It is generally accepted that this usually results in a product having properties of greater value than those of the parental strains combined additively. The phenomenon has been termed 'hybrid vigour'.

The present discussion seeks to determine whether there may exist a useful analogy to the above concepts in the intellectual sphere. Does the interaction of technologies result in a level of scientific fertility, or creativity, in excess of that which might be expected within individual disciplines? And, if so, how may such an interaction be encouraged?

This discussion will make no pretence to a qualitative originality. Many of the ideas which will be presented are already accepted by some individuals, and even in some scientific disciplines, though not in all. These ideas do, however, merit careful discussion and evaluation at the present time. If they meet widespread acceptance, consideration of their logical consequences in regard to the training of scientists is indicated.

Sources of creativity in contemporary genetics

In searching for the answer to this question it may be desirable to focus on a limited specific area of science. I have chosen for this purpose the field of fundamental genetics which currently is popularly, though inexactly, represented by the term 'molecular biology'. New concepts of fundamental importance are being generated in this field at an almost unprecedented rate.

It is immediately obvious that there is in this area a remarkable interplay between diverse sciences. This is well exemplified in the backgrounds of many of its leading figures.

Max Delbruck, considered by many to be the father of the field, is a physicist who entered biology. This particular combination will be seen to represent a recurring, though not exclusive, theme.

Sir MacFarlane Burnet, a pioneer in many areas of experimental biology, father of the clonal selection theory of antibody formation, and of the concept of immunologic tolerance, for which he was awarded a Nobel prize, represents within his background the productive integration of medicine, genetics, bacteriology, virology and immunology. There can be little question that Burnet would have been unable to exert his great influence, and stimulation to experimental biology and medicine had he not been himself a master of these diverse disciplines.

Following the tradition of Delbruck are Luria, Dulbecco, Crick, Watson, Brenner and Benzer. This group of investigators, whose output, and that of their students, embraces a large proportion of the important discoveries in the field of molecular biology, all represent the fusion between a background in some branch of physics and a branch of biology, usually genetics.

Luria, who was largely responsible for the introduction of the concept of 'general virology', that is, virology as a branch of biology as opposed to its more practical implications, exemplifies this type of background particularly well, being trained in medicine, physics, genetics and virology. A somewhat similar interaction is seen in the background of François Jacob, a physician who was introduced into the field of virology and genetics by André Lwoff, himself a productive hybrid between protozoology and virology.

The relationship between creativity and diversity of background

The above examples, which could be multiplied, but to no purpose, would appear to indicate that important scientific creativity in this area has been closely associated with an interaction of diverse branches of science. The closeness of the association, that is the quantitative correlation which may exist between creativity and diversity in the background of the creative scientist, would perhaps be a worth-while subject for investigation. An obvious difficulty in such an investigation is the difficulty in defining and assessing 'creativity'. Indeed, careful investigation of this problem would require that 'creativity' also be subject to quantification. This might be approachable by the use of a 'creativity index' derived not only from the number of publications produced in a given period of time but also from some quantifiable estimate of their importance. The latter could at least to a degree be estimated by the frequency with which each paper is quoted. Such methods may be adequate for assessing the creativity of the bulk of the scientific community; however, they would fail to do justice to those whose extreme creativity places them far ahead of their time. Such individuals may produce only a few key publications, whose importance will not be immediately apparent, or accepted, and which may therefore be only rarely quoted in the years immediately following their publication.

A second difficulty which will arise in any attempt to quantify the degree of correlation between creativity and diversity of background is that one would like to investigate the interaction of these variables independently of other critical factors, such as, for example, native endowment or 'intelligence'. This can of course be carried out by application of standard methods of statistical analysis, i.e. analysis of variance; however, measurement of intelligence *per se* leaves much to be desired.

For the above reasons the present discussion must remain qualitative, and speculative.

If we are to assume a positive correlation between scientific creativity and the interaction of technologies, an assumption which will be implicit in the ensuing discussion, there are then two major questions which remain to be answered. First, what are the causal relationships involved in this association: Does scientific creativity tend to appear more commonly in those scientists trained in diverse technologies; or, do creative scientists feel a need for a close understanding of a variety of disciplines?

This question is not easy to answer at the present time. The ultimate answer may be found in a combination of the above alternatives. In other words, it seems likely that creative individuals tend to feel a need for investigation of a series of diverse disciplines; but also, that the less intrinsically creative individual will find his efforts to produce new and important scientific information greatly facilitated if he is fortunate enough to possess a background in two or more diverse technologies.

The quantitative resolution of the above two alternatives is fortunately not critical for a discussion of the second, and last, question to be raised. That is, making the assumption that the interaction of technologies is both useful and desirable, how may we best encourage it?

Technological interaction within individuals or groups?

In attempting to answer the last question one might first consider whether it is necessary that the interaction of scientific disciplines should occur within the mind of given individuals; or would it be simpler and equally fruitful to encourage such interaction among different individuals, each of whom has his entire background in a single discipline? Although it is probable that both procedures may be beneficial, it may be suggested that there is currently an over-emphasis on the interaction of individuals in different disciplines, as opposed to interaction of different disciplines within the individual. Group thinking, although useful for the execution of complex projects of an applied nature, has not proved particularly useful for the generation of new ideas. There would appear to be an increasing realization that the latter type of thinking occurs more frequently within the mind of a single individual, subject to diverse influences.

A proposal

How then are we to facilitate the interaction of technologies within the minds of creative scientists? The following proposal is recognized not to be original in a qualitative sense; however, the assessment of its importance, and consequently its scope, is perhaps greater than has been the case heretofore.

It is proposed that governments, and foundations, might usefully consider the interaction of technologies to be the most underdeveloped area in their scientific training and fellowship programmes; and that support in this area might be expected to bear the richest fruits. If this supposition were accepted it would then appear logical to offer outstanding trained specialists in given technologies the opportunity of accepting two- to five-year fellowships for the acquisition of training and experience in second, or even third, disciplines.

Such training should be designed with due consideration for the special backgrounds of these senior individuals in order to avoid unnecessary duplication, and the relatively artificial stresses associated with selection processes within specialized fields.

For such a programme to be successful it would perhaps be helpful if the salary, security and prestige of such senior fellowships could compete successfully with that available in competing positions open to outstanding specialists. To avoid creating the adverse impression that the participants in such a programme were perennial students, with the possible implication that these individuals might be incapable of assuming normal degrees of responsibility, it would appear desirable that the fellows be given a new and distinctive identification. A title such as 'Senior Interdisciplinary Scientist', although rather cumbersome, might be suggested.

May we not anticipate, should such a proposal come to pass, a far greater nucleus of broadly trained scientists, whose understanding, transcending individual technologies, would give rise perhaps to a broader awareness of the common ground which unites all technologies, and which thus constitutes the essence of the process called scientific endeavour?

9

D. M. JAMIESON

The Encouragement of, and Preparation for, the Interaction of Technologies

The title of this essay immediately provokes a number of questions. Does such an interaction exist? Would it be surprising if such an interaction did exist? Assuming that there is an interaction, is it desirable, and, if so, how may it be encouraged?

Before addressing ourselves to these questions, it is at least helpful, if not absolutely necessary, that we understand what is meant by 'interaction of technologies'. In order that we can proceed on a common premise, the following definitions are proposed for the purpose of this paper. We shall consider as a technology any applied branch of a scientific discipline which is used for a practical purpose such as the production of goods and services. This is purposely a broad definition which permits inclusion of mathematics and the social and medical sciences in addition to the more commonly considered branches of engineering.

Next, and not superfluously, we shall define interaction. We shall distinguish between two types of interaction. Interaction Type A we shall define to be the existence of an idea or concept common to more than one basic discipline. Interaction Type B we shall define to be the need for the application of more than one technology to produce the desired object of some particular endeavour.

With these definitions as our starting point, we can turn to consideration of our initial question: 'Does such an interaction exist?' While given sufficient diligence, it would be possible to devote the remainder of our allotted 25,000 words to the presentation and careful documentation of many examples of both types of interaction in proof of their existence, we shall content ourselves with one example of each type of interaction. We can then invoke the established mathematical principle that the existence of a counter-example is sufficient to disprove a postulate, which in this case would be the assertion that no such interaction existed.

As an example of Type A interaction, consider the concept of positive and negative feedback. This concept has been familiar in control technology for a number of years. Recently, however, it has found application in a number of other fields. The extent to which this basic concept has spread is witnessed by the fact that at the 1964 Annual Meeting of the American Association for the Advancement of Science, held in Montreal, a whole day was given over to a symposium entitled, 'Positive Feedback in General Systems'. The symposium was sponsored by the Society for General Systems Research, and during the course of the day, papers were read by economists, psychologists, psychiatrists, political scientists and biologists, in addition to engineers; all presenting examples of the feedback principle in their particular field.

For an example of Type B interaction, consider the placing in orbit of an artificial satellite. To achieve this end, the chemist or chemical engineer with his knowledge of fuels must collaborate with the mechanical engineer with his knowledge of structures and vibration. Electronics technology is required for guidance, and applied mathematics for the calculation of velocities to obtain the desired path. All these specialties along with others must be brought to bear on the problem and made to combine smoothly if the project is to be successful.

Resting our case for the existence of both types of interaction upon these examples, we can turn to our next question: Is the existence of such interactions surprising? In this portion of the essay we shall also be concerned with the 'divisions and barriers between different technologies' mentioned in the terms of reference for this paper. It is the author's contention that these interactions are not only not surprising but are to be expected. For, after all, the various technologies are but applications of various branches of science, and these branches of science stem from a common root. Since this is so, one would expect the basic scientific disciplines to share a common methodology and to have areas of overlapping interest. Why then should 'divisions and barriers' have arisen? These divisions and barriers are artificial in the sense that they have been imposed by man in his division of science into the various basic disciplines. Yet, these divisions have been forced upon man by the very success of science and the scientific method. Today, with the ever-increasing number of people engaged in scientific pursuits, new knowledge and new discoveries, some important and many trivial, are increasing exponentially. To sort the wheat from the chaff, to stay up to date and maintain a mastery of even one basic field, requires a man or woman of outstanding ability. For a single mind to comprehend, command and be aware of the latest work in all fields of science (not even considering the myriad technological applications of these disciplines) is today not possible even if the present day included such legendary figures as Gauss, Newton or Aristotle.

Faced with this paradox that increasing specialization is being forced upon us whilst we acknowledge that technologies are based on various scientific disciplines springing from a common root so that we might expect ideas and techniques of our area to be useful in another, what are we to do? Whether we do anything or not depends upon what answer we give to the third of our questions: Are interactions of technologies desirable? This is not a good question. For what each person considers desirable is a matter of individual judgement and so we can hardly expect to get an objective answer. One need only consider one example of interacting technologies—a missile with a nuclear warhead—and ask whether this is a desirable end-product. The storm of discussions involving political, moral and ethical considerations which such a question precipitates, takes us far beyond the scope of this paper.

Let us modify our question to: Are such interactions of technologies fruitful in producing new and richer technological products?—the goods and services of our definition. We can now answer with an unqualified yes. In our example of a Type A interaction, we cited the application of the concept of feedback in fields quite divergent from its original application in engineering. Such applications have proved most fruitful, for example, in giving a greater insight into the ecology of pond life, and so lead to an improved technology of manipulating this pond life to man's desired purpose. Again, consider the realization of a flood control project. Here, if the project is to be successful and to be carried out efficiently, you must have the co-operation of a number of specialists. Clearly, you must have the services of a meteorologist or climatologist to estimate for you the maximum precipitation to be expected, then you must have a civil engineer to design and build the dam or dams required. Probably you also require the services of an erosion expert to advise on ground cover planting to control the flow of water in the catchment area.

Another intriguing example of work by groups from various disciplines is in homeostatic prosthetic devices. Various groups combining the talents of engineers and doctors are engaged in devising techniques and tools for those persons who have lost a limb or use of an internal organ. As an example, suppose a person has lost a hand, then if it were possible to pick up the electrical signals from the severed nerve-endings, it would be possible to amplify the signals, monitor them and use them to control the function of a power-operated artificial hand. The solid-state physicist also plays a part in this, for it is his work which provides the basis for microminiturization of the electrical devices essential for such projects. The other example of work in this field concerns diabetic patients where sensors would be implanted in the patient's pancreas to monitor the blood sugar and supply injections of insulin of the right quantity when required.

As we can see, then, both Type A and Type B interactions can provide very fruitful results. Further, extrapolating past experience into the future, the trend is towards increasing complexity in our civilization. Some people may deplore this, but whether we are in favour or not, the trend seems inexorable. However tempting, the simplicity of the golden age (the joys of which sometimes obscure the realities of unremitting toil by the many for the pleasure of the few) seems fated never to return. We must find ways of controlling the awesome powers which science has placed at the command of the politicians. We must find ways of providing living space and sufficient food for an expanding population. Ideally, we would like to free all mankind of the back-breaking toil to which some underprivileged primitive peoples are committed merely to scratch out a bare existence.

If we are to do all these things, then clearly technology must play its part in increasing the productivity of the individual man and the organized society of collective man. That such improvements in technology will lead to complex systems requiring interacting technologies (however much we do and should strive for simplicity), seems inevitable. That technology should strive for efficiency by exploiting both Types A and B interaction seems imperative.

How can this exploitation be encouraged? We may receive some guidance by examining the organization and performance of existing and prior interdisciplinary groups. Such groups can serve a double purpose for not only do they permit the collection of experts of various disciplines to attack a problem as in our Type B interaction, but by permitting the free interchange of ideas among our group of experts, they encourage the application of an established technique or concept in one field in some new and fresh endeavour, thus providing a Type A interaction. Since we are concerned with the provision or outline of some organization devoted to the encouragement of interacting technologies, we will restrict the following discussion to consideration of organized groups collected for a purpose. This eliminates from consideration the collaborative efforts of two individuals of different disciplines who, from personal friendship or mutual interest, combine to attack a problem of joint interest. Also, we shall restrict ourselves to the problem of how to encourage interaction of technology and not permit ourselves to become involved in the larger problem of how does one organize a research and development organization. This latter problem is receiving considerable attention in the U.S.A. with a group at M.I.T. being funded to study the management of research and development, and the important business magazine *Fortune* running a series of articles on the topic. It is being realized that the mere assemblage of scientists and technologists and the provision of facilities and equipment is not sufficient. Something else is needed. Perhaps part at least of this something else is akin to the topic of our paper, the provision for an interaction of technology and of the scientific disciplines.

One of the earliest documented efforts at organizing interdisciplinary groups as such was the establishment of operational research groups during the second world war, to advise military commanders. Started in Great Britain to make effective use of the radar developed by the team led by Sir Robert Watson Watt, the idea spread to other fields of battle and to other countries, being adopted, for example, by United States forces.

After the end of hostilities, this new and promising technique was employed by industry and business to improve their operations and policies. It was also hoped by some that it would be the nucleus of an effort to encourage the interaction of technologies and the interaction of scientific disciplines.

This hope, however, has not been fully realized. Certainly a great deal of fruitful work was done and continues to be done in the field of operational research by groups composed of scientists and technologists drawn from various disciplines. The technology, however, has tended to develop as a field in its own right with individuals (usually with a catholic interest) practising operational research as a profession. This tendency had led to the image of operational research as a tool-box of techniques to be applied to a wide variety of management and technological problems. The existence of such a tool-box is very valuable. Additions to the tool-box, together with the training of skilled individuals knowledgeable in the selection and use of the correct tool, is valuable and to be encouraged. However, development along these lines tends to disqualify operational research as a vehicle for the encouragement of interaction of the technologies.

It has been found throughout the history of science that an individual branch of science becomes most effective when it is based on a carefully reasoned theoretical foundation. Consider the case of astronomy. Astronomers or astrologers (in early days the two terms were close to synonyms) had collected mountains of observations, but it was not till Kepler came along with his three laws that there was some order and reliable application of the data. Later still, Newton's law of gravitation provided the key theoretical basis upon which a sound celestial mechanics could be based. Not only did these discoveries present a more useful vehicle for prediction, but they were much simpler and yet more elegant than the complex Ptolemaic explanation of planetary motion involving epicycles.

It would be helpful then if there was a theoretical foundation for our efforts to encourage interaction of technologies. Since this is a new endeavour, it has not yet developed a clear rigorous foundation. Within the past ten years, a society to promote such work has been initiated by a group of individuals interested in interdisciplinary work. This society ('Society for General Systems Research') has amongst its stated aims: the investigation of the isomorphy of concepts, laws and models in various fields and the encouragement of useful transfers from one field to another. Additional aims include the development of adequate theoretical models in fields which lack them and the promotion of unity of science through improving communication among specialists.

Had all these aims been achieved, then we would need to look no further for a theoretical basis for our interacting technologies. But, this effort is a new one and so far progress in the shape of a well-developed theoretical model for general application has been slow in evolving. The main point is that the start has been made, and if we wish to encourage interaction in technology, we would do well to support and promote work of this nature.

Finally we must turn, as in so many things, to the individual. What sort of individual can we expect to be active in producing interaction in technology or providing a theoretical foundation upon which it can rest.

Examination of individuals who are active in this field and making significant contributions suggests that he should be competent and well trained in one scientific discipline in which he has gained professional recognition. Coupled with this, he must have a broad understanding of science in general so that he can converse intelligently with colleagues expert in fields other than his original specialty. And, of course, he must have the desire to put this training and ability to work in interdisciplinary tasks and research.

Individuals with these qualities at present exist both inside and outside universities. Within academic circles, there is perhaps more encouragement or at least more latitude for such individuals to join with like minds in pursuing interdisciplinary work. This opportunity, together with the communication network between groups provided by organizations such as the Society for General Systems Research (which has a membership drawn from fifteen countries throughout the Americas, Asia and Europe), augurs well for the establishment of a sound theoretical foundation for interdisciplinary work.

How may industry and government put such theoretical work to use and indeed achieve that interaction of technology which will lead to increasingly fruitful results? One method would be to organize groups of experts in various disciplines and include within the group as catalysts (possibly in charge of the group) individuals of accepted competence in their own field, but with that catholic scientific interest which enables them to contribute to other fields. Such individuals might well be a combination of the European-type academic and the American-type pragmatist. In the past, industry and government have looked to the liberal arts generalists for their leaders. They may continue to do so in the future, but if we are to achieve interaction in technology, we shall require, at some responsible level in the organization, the liberal scientific generalist, a person with some founding in the humanities, a sound scientific training which gives him grounding in the basic disciplines and methods of science and who will also be of professional stature in one of the basic disciplines. To be a success as a catalyst or innovator of interdisciplinary work, he will also have to be able to co-operate with and obtain co-operation from his interdisciplinary group.

It may seem that we are asking rather a lot from our liberal scientific generalist, but such people already exist, and, with encouragement, more could be developed. They will probably always be a small group and, like a fine wine, will probably require a few years for development (practising their professional specialty?) before being at their best.

Whether degree-granting institutions should provide us with graduates who are interdisciplinary specialists is a moot point. At present the prospect of a new graduate with a doctorate or good honours degree in interdisciplinary technology is not too appealing. Even the very good graduate would need some seasoning. Certainly a great deal of care would have to be taken to ensure that the end-product was a well-rounded man and not a jack-of-all-trades.

On the other hand, social and economic pressures may make it necessary for the individual to have some professional recognition as someone whose avocation lies in interdisciplinary work. Perhaps one solution would be to follow a course of study which included sufficient material to prepare the student for interdisciplinary work, but also included enough material for him to be accepted as a professional in one of the established disciplines. Then, after practising in this field for a period of time and establishing his or her liking for, and ability in, interdisciplinary research, the candidate could be licensed by some board akin to that used by the medical profession.

This whole area of preparation for participating in the interaction of technologies could be the subject of a completely new paper. Suffice it to say that at present a few individuals are working along the lines of improving communications between technological fields and being active in many disciplines. If we are to try to increase their numbers, this area of formal and informal preparation will require intensive study.

In summary, then, we have demonstrated the existence of interaction of technology by citing specific examples where it is occurring today. We have further shown that such interactions are to be expected, for the various technologies are but the applied branches of the scientific disciplines which themselves come from a common root. We have then examined ways in which fruitful interactions might be encouraged, and what kind of individuals one would expect in this field. In conclusion, we would like to quote Hans Selye: 'In science there are no small limited fields, only small limited scientists. In nature, every field flows over into all adjacent subjects.'

10

SIMON WOOLF

Abstraction of Technologies

Technologies meet most frequently in their application. Someone designing, say, a petrol engine contends with the technologies of fuel, lubrication and machinery. Sometimes design problems of this kind are fully determinate: suppose, for instance, that one is concerned with designing a tie-rod for use in a corrosive atmosphere, then given data such as strength and cost of various materials and protective treatments, and the interest rates on capital, it would be easy, if tedious, to calculate the most economic solution. But much more often design problems are not determinate—they have an element which (in the time available) is not calculable. If we add to the previous problem that the tie-rod must fit into its surroundings so as to be pleasant to the eye, or add instead that the cost of the joint at the end of the tie-rod is significant, then the problem is beyond calculation—in the one case because one cannot calculate aesthetic factors, and in the other because time and data is not available to solve what is, in principle, a determinate problem. It does not really matter why the problem cannot be determined: whatever the cause, if it is indeterminate then its solution becomes a matter of judgement rather than calculation. It is the important rather than unimportant problems which are of this indeterminate nature. Parliament discussing some measure which affects all our lives does so necessarily in general terms: a shopkeeper can, by contrast, decide with absolute precision what an account should be.

The process of abstraction

In any situation there is, on the one hand, the reality, with real physical objects, and in our minds an idea of the physical and environmental situation which is essentially an abstraction of it. The latter is never complete, and is always to some extent inaccurate—brick carries in itself its history and physical shape down to the minutest blemish, but our idea of it for a great many purposes is that of a perfect rectangular block. It is convenient to speak of varying degrees of abstraction, a high degree being one in which much information is discarded, and a low degree of abstraction implying greater detail. This immediately raises the problem in abstraction of relevance and importance. To abstract the information in a report by tearing out alternate pages is not, on the whole, likely to yield a satisfactory abstraction of the material in the report. Rounding off the last digits of a series of numbers is, on the other hand, often a useful and correct procedure. Unfortunately, a ready statistical or mechanical means of abstraction is not available and frequently the first serious difficulty is to decide what information is relevant and, of the relevant information, what is important. A test of the usefulness of an abstraction is its generality.

There are, of course, a few established techniques for abstracting information. First is the use of mathematics to summarize a situation, and this of course is very important, opening the door to all the powerful means of operating on mathematical expressions. Similarly, when considering a physical shape or layout, drawings of various degrees of detail are often used. In deciding what is irrelevant or unimportant, we discard information or approximate it, as we represent an ordered set of numbers by a few numbers each rounded off, or state a size approximately. This approach may include the complete omission of some facets of a situation. It is common, for instance, to omit questions of colour and surface texture from a decision about the interior of a house, because these can be decided independently (that is, at a lower level of abstraction). A very useful example of abstraction is inherent in the language of planning: in building, for instance, one talks of 'services'; thus grouping together all the pipes and wires along which water, gas, electricity and telephone conversations flow—essentially the grouping of similar things to develop a mental technique. The use of the word 'services' in building design, with its obvious extension to the circulation of people and goods in a building, means that the language itself illustrates the unity of behaviour, and suggests a certain unity in the solution. One can consider the installation of a drain in a building as an isolated problem of collecting the drainage from a number of points in a complicated physical shape, or one can regard it as part of general problem of distributing men and materials through the building as they flow in and out, and it is the latter sort of technique that is likely to lead to a successful building.

The role of abstraction in technology

The development of chemical engineering forms a good example of the value of abstractions in reducing the apparently unrelated activities which make up the chemical industry to an ordered body of knowledge. This happened at the beginning of this century and can be credited to George E. Davis of this country and Arthur D. Little of the U.S.A., who realized that the operations involved in the manufacture of chemicals could be reduced to a limited number of unit processes and unit operations. Examples of these are heat and mass transfer, or filtration and distillation. These processes and operations could then be studied in an increasingly abstracted form and reported in a more general way. The results obtained could then be applied to specific industrial problems.*

In many ways scientific theories are abstractions of experimental or observed facts, but there is a fundamental difference: the scientific theory must so abstract the fact that it can make predictions which then can be tested, and although it is no doubt aesthetically more satisfactory if the theory is simple, this is not an essential. If Newton's laws of motion had turned out to be formulae a yard long, from the scientific point of view they would still have been used if they were the simplest expressions that could be found. This is because science is devoted to investigation, and one can investigate using highly complex techniques, but when the activity is not investigation but design or synthesis (the taking of complex and indeterminate decisions), one must use simpler ideas and expressions. The test then of the abstraction for decision-taking is, first, that it should help in making decisions. It must, of course, have a certain accuracy, but the prime necessity is simplicity. It is rather like the soldier's dictum that a bad plan carried out with determination is better than no plan at all; equally the alternative to an inaccurate abstraction may be a chance decision by tossing a coin (often enough the most reasonable way of making a decision).

The writing of technologies in terms of differing modes or levels of abstraction suggests a certain unity of approach to abstraction. In one form, this involves simply a unity of language with, say, symbols for equivalent things made recognizably similar. From another point of view, it requires that the relative importance of the data should be borne in mind. It is often all too easy when dealing with unimportant matters to present or conceive of the data as representing absolute and unalterable requirements, so that a particular aspect of the problem is catered for at the expense of others. For example, it is not uncommon to see a modern factory with a shell designed with all the simplicity and elegance

*I am indebted to Mr. L. Holliday for this example.

that might grace any great concourse, but which in a factory ignores completely the array of pipes and ducts and pieces of plant that are properly suspended from the roof structure, and which negate the very essence of the design.

A common approach to abstraction in different technologies leads ultimately to a transverse system of parallel techniques, each representing a level or mode of abstraction and 'parallel' to mathematics which serves so many technologies. Such transverse techniques would, of course, be a ready path for the dissemination of information derived from one technology amongst other technologies.

There are one or two levels at which such correspondence in abstracttion is readily recognizable as existent or easy to achieve: an engineer's education, for example, commonly covers a range of subjects such as electricity, surveying, strength of structures, hydraulics and so on. It is a common enough observation how frequently one seems to be doing similar things in different fields; how often one is integrating the area under a curve; how often networks of jointed rods or pipes or electric conductors are being considered along lines which are not altogether dissimilar; how often one is optimizing measurements or energy levels in structures or costs in design along lines which are often identical. Although the generality of the mathematics is clear, nevertheless the subjects still go their own ways at the moment. Considering again the example of a factory, it is useful to have data for all the individual services of optimum spacing of runs and outlet points, and cost data for differing spacings, and there would be value in co-operative investigations of the optimum for the distribution of groups of services, since in some types of buildings, groups of services with common outlet points have to be routed through the structure.

Non-mathematical abstraction

When mathematics is applied to technologies, it states (however imprecise the data) a precise relationship between the symbols describing the data, and it develops theorems relating the symbols. A parallel process for non-mathematical abstractions may be possible and may be useful. Two such theorems have been suggested: that the level of abstraction should match the generality of the decision being taken, and, as a corollary, the levels of abstraction of the various technologies or other data should match one another. It has now become clear that there is a need for several parallel developments:

1. The development of techniques of abstraction.
2. The writing of the technologies at varying levels of abstraction, corresponding to the generality of the decisions in which the technologies are involved.
3. The development of theorems relating abstractions.
4. The development of processes of decision-taking so that they can, where it is possible, be more specific.

It is surprising how often one looks back after a long struggle to arrive at a decision to realize that many aspects of the result were inevitable and might, had one but seen more clearly, have been written down from the start. It is, of course, this difficult but determinate or partly determinate class of problem that is most successfully attacked by the processes of abstraction described above. Specifically, one would hope to be able to decide on a number of levels of abstraction at which successive decisions might be taken: the data would all be abstracted to match the most abstract level, the appropriate decision would be taken and worked backwards to the next level of abstraction at which appropriately abstract data would be introduced to provide the solution at that level. One decides at one level that a town should be in a particular place, at the next level the broad outlines of the town, the location of centres of industry and pleasure and so on, at the next the precise layout of the streets and so backwards until over the years one writes in the minutest detail of each habitation. One proceeds from the physical facts of the situation through abstraction to decision, from decision by iteration to less abstract decision, and finally back to the physical fact of the town in place. This is the outline of how one might decide: how to fill it in and whether much more detail is possible in general terms is for the future.

Technologies also interact in a much more direct way by means of those technologies which cut across others. The most powerful of these at the moment are probably those associated with mathematics, notably the computer industry which will solve problems for a great range of technologies and so provide a means for the exchange of information via the computer industry, which becomes aware of similar problems in different fields. Similarly, manufacturers of parting agents for casting, and manufacturers of lubricants and fuels will assist diverse industries and transfer information between them. In a sense all industry interlaces in this way, and it is surprising how wide a field one does contact even when engaged in relatively isolated activities.

The future

A technology exists to enable some activity to proceed, and the condition for the use of the product of that technology is that some decision is taken to use it. Since decisions are made by means of abstractions it is therefore inevitable that the technology should be described in terms of abstractions suited to the decision in which the technologies are involved. These abstractions are one of the means of communication and interaction between the technologies. They are less definite and less informative than the data from which they derive but they are important because of their use in decisions. It may be useful to develop on a more conscious level the means of abstracting and the techniques of using abstractions. We want, so to speak, a mathematics of the indefinite.

11

D. A. WALKER

The Integration of Technologies

In the most advanced parts of our present civilization, technology holds a position reminiscent of the dominant one it occupied in the Stone Age. Then, as now, society was built around a group of skills and crafts with aesthetic activities playing a supporting role. It is fortunate for our sense of perspective that, in between these two eras, about the time of the Renaissance, the cultural pendulum demonstrated that it could swing in the other direction. Today, as we learn to control our social environment, and with it this cultural pendulum, with a precision unimagined two generations ago and unimaginable two generations hence, we are faced with such questions as: Where shall we strike the balance? Answers to questions of this kind are not found in a day, but it is now widely agreed that we must again make room for a flourishing aesthetic culture. Since the pendulum has already swung so far towards a materialistic culture, the question thus reduces to one of: How are we to contain the over-swing?

There are, it seems to me, only two ways of controlling the proliferation of technological activity. Either we intervene in the process of supply and demand and, in effect, agree to do without some of the advances that are within our grasp; or we set about developing a more vigorous and efficient technology that can satisfy our demands without becoming the very *raison d'être* of our society. As is our custom, we shall probably adopt a compromise course, taking in something from each of these expedients but, in doing so, we must recognize a limitation in the former. It is simply that, while we can adopt nationally a policy of planned intervention in the so-called 'natural order' of supply and demand in certain expensive fields, if we are to take proper account of the pressure of international competition over a wide range of fields, a similar policy would have to be agreed and implemented on a worldwide scale. This would be an exercise demanding a degree of international co-operation and restraint to which we are not yet fully accustomed. In view of this limitation, which is likely to be with us for some time, we should, perhaps, be wiser to concentrate the major part of our effort on the latter course of developing a more vigorous and efficient technology.

Now, the invigoration of technology is a fascinating but vast project; one in which interactions of all kinds will play a vital but sometimes unacknowledged part. We can expose this role by adopting at the outset a broad perspective as follows. Firstly, we have two main lines of attack: (a) to make better use of our existing technology and, (b), to increase the rate of generation of new ideas. Secondly, to avoid misdirecting our aim in applying these, we can choose to recognize two distinct kinds of technology, which we shall call operational and scientific technology. To define these terms more fully, operational technology is associated with the functions of design, product development, manufacture and nowadays management itself and even marketing; it is applied by teams of specialists who are often highly skilled in the exploitation of known techniques. On the other hand, while exploitation is the keynote of operational technology, the scientific counterpart is characterized by exploration. The function of this branch is to supply operational technology with the techniques, materials and devices that it needs and, as such, it is closely connected with, but without the detached attitude of, pure science. In short, while operational technology helps to achieve a specific goal, scientific technology provides the tools. A technologist may, at different times, perform both functions; nevertheless, the difference is sufficient to suggest two target areas, one for each of our lines of attack, namely, better efficiency in operational technology and better innovation in scientific technology.

Let us first look at operational technology. Being more closely identified with the fulfilment of a demand, the final product, it tends to receive more attention than its scientific counterpart. The two brightest spotlights on it at present are the application of a now established science, operational research, to the planning and administration of projects, and the application of a relatively new discipline, information science, to communications. Operational research, developed during the last war, has come a long way, ever since the oft-quoted success of one of its techniques, network analysis, in the Polaris missile project. University departments and consultants specializing in these techniques are a familiar part of the scene as are the symposia and the books that are adding to the already formidable mass of theory and case-history. It seems fairly safe to assume that, before long, every major project involving operational technology will be planned in this way. This, in its best form, is efficiency *par excellence*; but it cannot achieve its full impact without correspondingly efficient lines of communication. As manifestations of this new emphasis on communications we have the S.D.I. system, or Selective Dissemination of Information, and the Industrial Liaison Officer scheme of the D.S.I.R. Both of these, incidentally, are of infinitely more use to the operational technologist than to his scientific colleague, whose main job in connexion with these schemes is to develop them. No longer is it, in this field, a question of aims; only the formidable but relatively straightforward problem of implementation remains.

What kind of interactions can be expected to happen between operational technologies? Any operation worth the name demands the use of more than one technology and, in those circumstances, interactions are, of course, inevitable; but it is important to recognize that they are, nevertheless, of an *ad hoc* nature. That is to say, the existence of a link between two operational technologies depends on the project, and will, in general, last only for as long as it is required by the project. Interactions between operational technology and scientific technology are equally ephemeral; the moment a tool becomes obsolete the link disappears. Why is this? The traditional structure of the organization of this field gives us our clue. Well suited to the philosophy of operational technology is the concept of the team, which might consist of a number of people, each of whom is skilled in the exploitation of a different technology. It is the widespread use of the team which, in fact, renders unnecessary the maintenance of permanent bridges in the form of, say, inter-disciplinary specialists. The atmosphere of exploitation, then, which is characteristic of the goal-oriented environment, certainly produces interaction but it does not provide the best climate for interaction to develop into integration.

Turning now to the field of scientific technology, or, as it is more often called, applied science, we shall encounter a different kind of interaction. The sole function of this field is, in effect, to supply new ideas, and because both the degree of success and the time required are substantially independent of the manpower available, such an activity is virtually unplannable in the operational sense. Innovation is the product of a highly individual quality known as creativity, which cannot be examined in an impersonal way. Unaccustomed, as most of us are, to studying the world through man, we tend, when adopting this approach, to hamper ourselves with a number of inhibitions. Nevertheless, because creativity is the very foundation of scientific technology, we must take this bull by the horns, and while not expecting to topple it, at least hope to discover something of its powerful nature.

Before we do so, however, let us look at an important feature, common to all technology, namely specialization. There is much head-shaking these days over the evils of specialization, but, once we recognize our two kinds of technology, it becomes clear that, in the operational field, specialization has always been a feature. Far from being a new and unfortunate characteristic that must be curbed, it has been part of, and beneficial to, operational technology ever since the time of primitive man; hence the team concept. The fact that science, and, with it, scientific technology is nowadays also becoming over-specialized has served admirably to confuse the functional difference between these two kinds of technology. It has also obscured the fact that two different forces are responsible for specialization. In the matter of learning skills we all have our limitations—if only because life is short. For the operational technologist to adopt a more universal and philosophic approach would, therefore, merely restrict his ability to exploit selectively, and to the full, the extremely complex skills we expect of him today. 'Jack-of-all-trades and master of none' has, in no other field, a truer ring. On the other hand, the growing fragmentation of science is not an inherent characteristic. Professor Auger has recently expressed the opinion that there is a limit to man's powers of conceptual thought; but no one has yet suggested that such a limit has already been reached. The prestige-motivated 'invisible colleges' of Derek De Solla Price and the 'schizmogenic' language difficulty outlined by Margaret Mead each undoubtedly play their part in encouraging specialization in science. But the success of interdisciplinary studies, such as materials science and operational research itself, encourage one to believe that this field is not the natural home of specialization. If this is the case, would we not simply be wasting our time if we attempted to fight specialization on its home ground, operational technology? Would it not be better to accept, and indeed exploit by teamwork the superficial nature of the interaction in the operational field and to concentrate on achieving an integration-in-depth in the field of scientific technology? In the discussion that follows I shall try to show how creativity can bring this about.

Creativity is wrapped in almost impenetrable mystique. Untaught, and regarded by most as unteachable, it has become a sort of deity which we are reluctant to understand and which we reverently worship. Nevertheless, it is, I believe, not only possible but urgently desirable for us to break down this mystique and formulate ways of inculcating in the technologist this highly prized faculty. Unfortunately, his formal educational experience is of no help. Beyond the infant school, with its enlightened emphasis on creativity, the thread is neglected, even in the humanities, and is all but lost in the fact-learning scramble that we impose upon the pupil. All the influences we exert on the budding technologist are designed to encourage him towards acquiring a rational, so-called 'scientific', attitude. In the end, rational thought, instead of taking its rightful place as a backcloth against which he evaluates creative thought, becomes in him the major, and eventually a sterile, mode of expression itself. True, we are beginning to correct this one-sided development by delaying specialization and by introducing 'liberal studies' in scientific education. But wide experience, as we shall see later, is not enough unless it is linked with the creative attitude, and this is seldom pointed out as a factor common to both cultures. Is it really so impossible to adopt a more positive approach to creativity throughout our scientific educational system? And, for those who have already passed through it, is it not possible for them to rediscover the creative attitude they possessed before it was sacrificed to rationalism?

There is little wonder, in view of our upbringing, that there exist numerous misconceptions about creativity. One of the most common of these is that it makes only rare appearances outside the arts, and, when it does, it belongs exclusively to pure science. The implication thus arises that only those capable of highly intelligent activities, such as conceptual thought, can hope to be creative. But recent research has shown that the correlation between intelligence quotient and creativity breaks down at the modestly high I.Q. level of 120. This result suggests that intelligence greater than I.Q. 120 can be superfluous for the purpose of innovation; which means that a creative attitude is within the capabilities of many more people than is generally supposed. Provided that the upper limits of his intelligence are such as to enable him to understand the idiom, a creative person can produce innovations in any field. It is no accident that creative scientists tend to design new instruments and write poetry with equal facility.

Almost every great innovator has speculated on the question of what is creativity; almost all agree on the presence of a common factor, namely, an irrational association of ideas. Indeed, such is the frequency with which this observation is made that it is something of a mystery in itself as to why so much mystery still surrounds our subject. This basic description of creativity clearly implies two aspects: an association of ideas, which everyone appreciates as an ingredient of invention, and an irrationality, which perhaps explains the mystery. We must be careful, however, not to dissociate these two aspects, for then each will tend to take on a relative significance in proportion to our degree of understanding of it. For instance, while on the one hand some see the rational interchange of existing information through communications or team-work, as in themselves productive of novel ideas, on the other hand there are those who believe that all inventions come out of the blue like those of the legendary Princes of Serendip.

Bearing in mind that it is not, by itself, sufficient, our first and easiest task in stimulating innovation in scientific technology is to set up a creative atmosphere. The underlying aim of the supervisor of a creative technologist should be to expose him to as wide a range of experience as he can take. This is achieved by encouraging him to discuss, with colleagues who will have been educated in a variety of disciplines, his problems, and theirs; by arranging laboratory seminars and encouraging attendance at external meetings; by emphasizing staff mobility, frequent changes of problem and 'diagonal' promotion as far as the minimum requirements of stability allow; and, generally, by avoiding the comfortable but sterile atmosphere that develops when each man is left to pursue his initial specialization along an ever-narrowing road. Where team-work is necessary, and scientific technology has its share of special skills, the team, however well it performs on its first project, should not be regarded as a permanent unit with a built-in success factor for all subsequent projects. Creativity is a disruptive force foreign to organization, and a strong organization can, and often does, suppress it. This phenomenon, a typical occurrence during the transition of a firm from its entrepreneur stage to its organization stage, can affect even the smallest unit of organization, because it comes from within. It is tempting for an employer in recruiting staff to demand 'relevant experience' in the hope of cutting corners during the settling-in period. Where creativity is concerned, however, all experience is potentially relevant, and, instead of recruiting a sound physicist or engineer, he may be persuaded to accept a mediocre man lucky enough to have had recent experience of the 'right' kind.

The competent research director will be familiar with these and many more techniques and pitfalls concerned with the generation of a creative atmosphere. Not so widely appreciated, this time on the part of the would-be innovator, is the conscious effort involved in developing a creative ethos in himself. Consistently, we can detect in the creative genius both a capacity for hard work and a universality of interests. It is conceded that the less-gifted innovator is unlikely ever to reach the pinnacles of these two attributes, but his goal is, nevertheless, clear.

This is not to say that he must flit like a butterfly from one superficial interest to the next, a process likely to stimulate innovation itself of a superficial character, but neither must he concentrate for too long on a narrow speciality, for this becomes, in the end, so unproductive of new ideas as to make him miss the creative boat altogether. In short, dilettantism without depth is as useless as virtuosity without variety.

Lest our would-be innovator is tempted to dismiss these generalities as empty slogans, let us offer him some more specific advice. Firstly, he must become less selective in his information intake. To this advice he might well retort that he is already absorbing as much as he can take. This objection, however, can be overcome once he is persuaded that, unlike his operational colleague, he need not retain all of the data in the surface of his memory for immediate access. Once a piece of information has been 'understood' he can, with practice, allow it to slip into the more unconscious regions of his memory store which have a more leisurely retrieval time. In other words he must develop the art of 'forgetting' and the complementary one of 'sleeping on a problem'. Next, he would be well advised to take an interest in the history of science and technology. Besides acquiring a broad interest in current technology, he can, in this way, expand his experience by another dimension, backwards in time. History is full of developments which, in their contemporary context, led nowhere, but which, by suggesting analogies or when re-interpreted in modern terms, often have a surprising relevance. Finally, he should remember that practice makes perfect. The simple acquisition of wide interests will be useless to him unless he also makes a habit of practising on a speculative basis the techniques of creative association that we shall discuss later. This way he can develop the kind of tentative iconoclasm that questions every aspect of orthodoxy and provides the starting point of all innovation.

Let us now consider the role of irrational thinking in creativity. This is the gremlin that causes difference between the smooth 'steamroller' progress of an operational plan and the erratic lurchings that characterize the history of technical innovation. A set of facts in the former context inexorably leads to a predictable conclusion; a set of facts in the latter may lie exposed for years, involved in several 'near misses', awaiting someone to apply an irrational association before they coalesce into an innovation. Now the observation that the subconscious stubbornly refuses to subscribe to rational thinking, as demonstrated, for instance, in dreaming, has often led to the assumption that an act of irrationality always derives from this region and therefore cannot be a conscious one. This explanation of irrationality in creativity in terms of the subconscious has been elaborated recently by Arthur Koestler in his book *The Act of Creation*. But is it not possible, indeed probable, that we can become capable of entirely conscious irrational acts if only we would permit ourselves? We can surely, like the humorist (who, as Koestler himself points out, uses in a more concious manner the same process of irrational association of ideas), develop conscious techniques of bringing about this process in the field of technology. True, in the case of the humorist this can lead to the sterile 'joke formula' and, in the case of the artist, to an over-exploited style; but novelty in technology is judged not by aesthetic but by functional standards. Although elements of these two standards combine in the much-neglected quality of elegance, the overriding criteria in technology must remain those of efficiency and relevance, and so here there is little risk of offending aesthetic standards.

We have now arrived at the important position of actually being able to make a start on filling in the missing element of scientific method. For four hundred years, scientists have sought a 'scientific' method of working—and so far have only succeeded in developing criteria by which their procedures should be judged, and a formal method of writing up their experiments that carefully conceals any hint of irrationality. There are two main reasons why creative technique has not developed in this field; one is that innovation in basic science, being of a fundamental, conceptual and often intangible nature, relies heavily on subconscious irrationality, and the other is that the criteria for judging the results are very often not available until much later. Since neither of these conditions exists in the field of scientific technology, is it not time for us to set aside our distrust of the irrational, our misplaced aesthetic reservations and our mystical attitude to creativity, and allow ourselves to explore the place of creative techniques in this field as a fundamental part of scientific method? By adding a few obvious techniques to those parts of Koestler's analysis for which we can reasonably substitute our idea of conscious irrationality for his of subconscious irrationality, we can, in fact, derive a useful list. Because these techniques could form a basis of a more comprehensive list constituting an important part of scientific method, a brief outline of each will be given. We should, however, remember that they represent means by which we can stimulate novel ideas through the avoidance of 'black-box' thinking. The relevance of these ideas must, of course, be judged against a strictly rational background.

Beginning then with the simpler techniques we have:

1. *Transposition.* The simple and direct transfer of a technique, material or device from one context to another, does not happen by itself but requires a creative effort proportional to the tenacity of its orthodox context. The channels for the transfer of 'hardware', such as non-stick coatings from space-capsules to saucepans, are nowadays quite good, and there are several journals and bulletins that can be said to exist almost solely for this purpose. But all this editorial effort will be wasted if the readers are over-selective in their information intake and over-impressed by orthodox contexts.

2. *Translation.* The conscious version of the classic story of Archimedes in his bath, this technique is distinguished from simple transposition by the slight change of emphasis it demands. In this case the orthodox context can appear very tenacious in that it has actually 'coloured' the technique, material or device. The translation of 'telephone network theory' from its named context to that of chemical processing, and the translation of 'electrical filter theory' from its orthodox context to that of complex mechanical systems, both involving a shift of emphasis, must have entailed a creative effort of this kind. To exploit this method, our would-be innovator needs to develop a total disregard for the jealous claims of the orthodox context, plus a practised eye for latent aspects of the technique, material or device that the context renders irrelevant to its special purpose.

3. *Inversion.* Carrying the shift of emphasis to its extreme we arrive at a technique that utilizes the creative potential of an entire reversal of concept. A man who, on being confronted with an electric motor, immediately sees the possibility of its functional inversion, the dynamo, is using this technique. Another man, operating on the verbal plane, might see a mechanical inversion suggested by the interchange of the words 'stator' and 'rotor'. In spite of the logician's insistence that a thing must either be *A* or *not-A*, we know, in our bones, that it can often be both. This apparent contradiction is, of course, brought about by a combination of tenacity of context and stereotyped language. Even the scientist has learned to live with schizoid concepts like wave-particle dualism. The practice, three times a day, as it were, of speculative inversions of the function, purpose, construction and terminology of whatever problem one happens to have handy will almost certainly yield something both novel and relevant.

4. *Combination.* Having tried unsuccessfully all the pat answers, the technologist may have to look no further than to some simple combination from the same list. The vision-phone, the turbo-prop engine, the analogue/digital computer and hundreds of other such hybrids are commonplace. Like transposition, this technique tends to yield solutions that, in retrospect, seem so obvious as to appear trivial and, as a result, it is often underestimated. Incidentally it is a technique which can fruitfully be turned inwards and the use of combinations of creative techniques themselves should not be overlooked.

5. *Extension.* This is a favourite technique of the rational-minded technologist and entails simply the imaginary extension, by interpolation or extrapolation, of a known but inadequate solution. Every technique, material or device that finds application over a wide range of problems is a candidate for this treatment. Frequently, and especially in a rapidly expanding technology, one finds that the required solution to a problem either occupies a gap in the range of a known solution or a place just beyond it. Sometimes the gap represents a fundamental limitation in that solution but, very often, the gap exists only because the problem itself is a novel one. The electromagnetic spectrum is a fertile illustration of this: there must be several people already speculating on possible uses of, say, coherent beams of X-rays.

Besides these easy, mechanical techniques there are four further methods that demand, as it were, a rather higher standard of irrationality. These may not be accessible to everyone but, nevertheless, their importance should be universally appreciated.

6. *Association by analogy.* Perhaps the most fruitful techniques of all, this process is nearly always detectable in some measure in the creative act. Examples abound; and the whole range of techniques from the electronic digital computer field that are currently being fed, by analogy, into the new fields of pneumatic and hydraulic logic devices is a typical case. Analogy has often been assumed to find its source of irrationality in the subconscious; the inventor is said to stumble upon his analogy 'accidentally'. True, the analogy is never presented on a plate and this is why our would-be innovator should keep his eyes open for it. The difficulty that scientists and technologists experience over this approach possibly stems from their deep-seated objection to the use of metaphor on the grounds that it is not in the interests of lucid communication. The writer, the artist and the composer all use metaphorical expression as a standard technique, and even if we do not like to communicate tech-

nology in this way, we should not forget that we can reason like an analogue computer as well as like a digital computer.

7. *Visualization.* A less well-known technique, this one aims at 'de-verbalizing' the situation. Any stylized mode of expression inhibits the creative fluidity that the mind, when released from its rational strait-jacket, seems to be capable of, and no one is more susceptible to the cliché effect than the man who thinks in words. We are, nowadays, so beset by the need to communicate that we forget just how inadequate a vehicle language can be for creative thinking. A classic illustration of this is the story of Kekulé who saw, in his mind's eye, the contortions of a chain molecule until, like a snake swallowing its own tail, it became what we know as the cyclic configuration of the benzene ring. Those who doubt that this technique can be achieved consciously need only remind themselves that the artist is obliged to work in this manner the whole time.

8. *Identification.* There are some imaginative engineers who make a habit of identifying themselves with mechanical objects. These people seem to be readily capable of projecting a personal spirit, a sort of *doppelgänger*, into a flowing liquid, a loaded fulcrum or even a non-passive element such as a transistor, and of 'feeling' what is going on. This invaluable knack enables the engineer to bring to bear on the problem all manner of personal experience, mostly by analogy, without having to disengage it from its orthodox context, namely himself. Einstein relates how, for years, during which he frequently speculated on the nature of space and time, he used to identify himself with a ray of light. The technique is really only an extension of the process that causes us to wince when we see someone crack his head on a low beam.

9. *Analysis versus synthesis.* Lastly, mention should perhaps be made of a process which is more a state of mind than a technique. If our would-be innovator spends some effort on attempting to define his problem in as many ways as he can and in trying to visualize its ideal solution, the very act of flitting between synthesis and analysis can often suggest a route from problem to solution.

It is hoped that these outlines will serve to illustrate the recurrent theme of interaction in creative technique. We have, as yet, hardly scratched the surface of this subject. Almost a subject in itself, for instance, is the quantitative measurement of creative potential in an individual—but that is another story. . . .

* * *

If one had to describe the aim of this thesis in one word, that word would be 'elegance'. This is a quality for which the pure scientist has always striven and on which the operational technologist is now beginning to set his sights. The lack of elegance in the area between these two fields has encouraged it to become fragmented and ill-defined. This, in turn, has deprived it of a recognized status and, so, the attention it badly needs. The remedy is not to rely heavily on attracting attention to this neglected no-man's-land by erecting superficial status-symbols, like degrees with special names, but to aim for an overall coherence and economy of effort that will give it a structural elegance of its own. It is obvious that such a quality cannot be imposed from outside but, in the power of creativity to bring about interactions of the sort that develop into permanent integrations, we have a force capable of generating this elegance from within. With the deliberate aim of sabotaging our inhibitions, I have tried to show that subconscious irrationality need not be our only source of creativity. I have tried also to show that it is possible to develop, with less mystique, creative techniques of idea association involving a conscious and controlled irrationality that any intelligent, but not necessarily brilliant, technologist can understand, practise and use. Let us, therefore, use them to integrate and invigorate our technology, to exploit our role as inventors to the world and eventually to lead us to a fuller and more balanced life.

12

EDWARD MANOUGIAN

Towards a Common Language for the Technologies

This brief dissertation is an effort to initiate a path of study which, in my opinion, would lead to an amalgamation of the existing technologies. It starts with the assumptions that the common ground of the various technologies (or sciences as I shall sometimes call them) is reason and the communication of reason through language. At first glance, the meaning of reason is clear. It is the active engagement of the mind towards the solution of a problem. The meaning of language, too, seems obvious. After all, we use it every day. In fact, judging from world politics, language is used more frequently than is reason. Admittedly, these comments are a bit naïve. But, as we know, looking further into the meaning of reason or language or, for that matter, any other word leads us ultimately into a vicious cycle and a philosophical attempt to justify our inadequacy. Let us, however, proceed a little further before throwing in the sponge.

Two forms of reasoning play a dominant role in present-day technology, namely, inductive reasoning and deductive reasoning. Of these, inductive reasoning is the more difficult to comprehend. Its habitat is the twilight zone of thought. It lives off of intuition, creativity and the ability to project into the future in some sense. Man has been able to make only feeble attempts at capturing it, one of these, by the way, being the Bayesian approach to statistics. I will not dwell long here but pass quickly to deductive reasoning. Here we stand on firmer ground. This is in part due to the fact that here we make the rules whereby the game is played. We decide what we will accept as truth beforehand and then proceed, often with ingenuity, along prescribed lines to prove or disprove a hypothesis. Frequently, to connect reason to reality, we call upon statistical methods, the vogue presently being that of hypothesis testing.

Let us turn our attention briefly to the role of language in the sciences. History shows that a science and its language evolve hand in hand. Why? Primarily foı the following reasons: (1) inadequacy of words or symbols in the pre-existing language; (2) clarity; (3) brevity;

(4) preciseness; (5) consistency in meaning. Not every technical language has been spurred by all members of this list. The most notable of those that have been so motivated is mathematics. In fact, towards the turn of the last century mathematics became so concerned with its language and modes of reasoning that a new science, metamathematics, was born and is at present in its adolescence. It has been able to tell mathematics to some extent which problems are solvable and which are not; what can be said in certain languages and what can't be said in those same languages; whether or not it is possible to have a statement in a given language and yet not be able to prove or disprove the validity of that statement. But, more important, it has broken many of the language barriers between mathematicians themselves.

This is all fine but what does it have to do with improving the fluidity between the technologies? Simply this. The barrier between the technologies lies to a great extent in the diversity of languages. It would seem, therefore, that a 'metatechnology' is needed to study these languages and find a common ground for them. Our objective, then, is to find a language tailored to suit the ordinary needs of all of the technologies. Since language serves as the written or spoken expression of reason, the language we seek will have to be at least rich enough to cope with inductive and deductive reasoning. Is this possible? It would appear that it is possible. The language which has evolved through the interplay of mathematics and metamathematics may well be the answer. It would therefore behoove us to take a look at this language and see if it will indeed serve the other sciences as well.

First, the difficulty of circular definitions is avoided by taking one or two notions as understood, without definition. There is some arbitrariness involved in the choice of the undefined notions. One productive approach is to take the notions of a set and of membership in a set as being undefined. Intuitively, a set is an abstract entity, i.e. existing in our minds, and consisting of a collection of abstract objects. We can specify a set by listing the objects in it or by giving a property common to only these objects. Each such object, then, is a member of the set. Sets usually are symbolized by using brackets of the type $\{\}$. For instance, if a, b, c, d symbolize the members of a set, then the set is written as $\{a, b, c, d\}$. Or, if $\varphi(x)$ means 'x has the property φ', then the set consisting of all those objects which have the property φ may be symbolized $\{x;\ \varphi(x)\}$ and read as 'the set of all x such that x has the property φ'. If x is a member of a set S then we write $x \varepsilon S$. Our undefined notions, then, are in essence symbolized by $\{\}$ and ε.

Suppose, for example, that I think of the pen in my hand and the cup on my desk as making up a set. Let p represent the pen and c the cup that I have in mind. Then this set is represented by $\{p, c\}$ (or what is the same $\{c, p\}$) and the fact that p is a member of $\{p, c\}$ is written $p \varepsilon \{p, c\}$. As another example let us think of all the robins alive at 12 noon (Greenwich time), 31 March 1965. Symbolically our thought can be represented by,

$$\{x;\ x \text{ is a robin alive at 12 noon, 31 March 1965}\},$$

where the property φ in this case is that of being a robin alive at 12 noon, 31 March 1965. Once the notions of set and membership in a set are taken as primitive, many languages may be developed, each depending upon the choice of symbols and the choice of requirements for the concatenation of these symbols into words, formulas and sentences. Furthermore, many logics may be developed depending upon the logical operations and the rules of inference chosen. For the moment we are interested in one of these languages and logics, namely that of everyday mathematics.

This language may be formulated by using, as symbols, the letters of the English alphabet along with various sorts of brackets. The words and sentences of this language are in many respects similar to the words and sentences of the English language. Thus, for simplicity in definition and discussion as well as deference to those who dislike learning new languages, let us assume them to be English words and sentences. The language of mathematics, however, will be displayed on occasion to give a glimpse of its identity. A formula will be taken to be an open sentence, that is, a statement of the form 'x is white' which becomes a sentence when a word (in this case a noun) is substituted for x. The logical operations are to a certain extent arbitrary and need be only one or two in number. However, it is convenient to start with a larger number of such operations, namely with the operations of conjunction, '$\wedge$', non-exclusive, disjunction, '$\vee$', implication, '$\Rightarrow$', logical equivalence, '$\Leftrightarrow$', negation, '$\sim$', universal quantification, '$\forall$', existential quantification, '$\exists$', and equality '$=$'. As for the rules of logical inference, we require only modus ponens and the usual rules for substitution.

Thus fortified, let us proceed further by introducing a few important ways in which sets may be combined. Let A and B represent two sets. The cartesian product of A and B, written $A \times B$, is $A \times B = \{<a, b>;\ a \varepsilon A_\wedge b \varepsilon B\}$ (or more properly $A \times B = \{x; x = <a, b>_\wedge a \varepsilon A_\wedge b \varepsilon B\}$). where $<a, b>$ may be defined to be $<<a>, <a, b>>$. Let us agree to write $A \times A$ as A^2. If all the elements of A are also elements of B, then A is said to be a subset of B, denoted, $A \subseteq B$. In terms of the language of mathematics, this is, $A \subseteq B \Leftrightarrow \forall x(x \varepsilon A \rightarrow x \varepsilon B)$. We write $A=B$ if and only if $A \subseteq B$ and $B \subseteq A$. That is, $A=B \Leftrightarrow A \subseteq B \wedge B \subseteq A$. The union of A and B denoted $A \cup B$ is, $A \cup B=\{x;\ x \varepsilon A\ .\ \vee\ .\ x \varepsilon B\}$. The intersection of A and B, written $A \cap B$ is, $A \cap B=\{x;\ x \varepsilon A\ .\ \wedge\ .\ x \varepsilon B\}$. The operations of union, intersection and cartesian product may be generalized to more than two sets.

We now turn our attention to a notion just as fundamental as the notion of a set, namely, that of a function. First, let us call the entity, $<a, b>$, defined above, an ordered pair, Then, a relation is a set of ordered pairs and a function is a many-one relation, i.e. no given first member is associated with more than one second member. This notion of a function lies hidden in many of the technologies. To expose it, let us take a closer look at it as it exists in mathematics. There are two sets associated with a function, namely the set of first elements of the ordered pairs in the function and the set of second elements. That is, if f denotes a function, then it may be written $f=\{<a, b>;\ a \varepsilon A \wedge b \varepsilon B\}$ where $A=\{a;\ a$ is a first element of an ordered pair in $f\}$, and $B=\{b;\ b$ is a second element of an ordered pair in $f\}$. (Frequently the fact that $<a, b> \varepsilon f$ is expressed by writing $b=f(a)$.) The set A above is called the domain of f and symbolized by $D(f)$, i.e. $D(f)=\{a;\ \exists b(<a, b> \varepsilon f)\}$. Similarly the set B is called the range of f, written $R(f)$, and defined by $R(f)=\{b;\ \exists a(<a, b> \varepsilon f)\}$. Often it is useful to explicitly express the domain and range of a function. To do this one may write $f\colon A \rightarrow B$ but more generally one writes $f\colon A \rightarrow Y$ where $D(f)=A$ and $R(f) \subseteq Y$.

Now let us turn our attention to the use of this language in other sciences. Physicists and electrical engineers are well aware of this language and are using it more and more. Biologists, as a rule, are unfamiliar with it. Its use in chemistry was conceived by A. Bartholomay[1.1] but little has been done since his paper of 1960. None the less chemistry is of especial interest because it has a rather unique language which makes frequent use of formulas and equations which somehow do not appear to be the same as the formulas and equations of mathematics. Furthermore, the biological sciences are making greater use of chemistry (viz. biological chemistry) so that the reconciliation of the languages of chemistry and mathematics would be a major step towards the unification of scientific language. Most of the remainder of this essay will be devoted to the illustration of how this may be accomplished. Being an illustration, it makes no claim to completeness or even ideal clarity. It only points to a direction.

We may begin by noting that chemistry makes special use of certain symbols in the alphabet for the representation of the chemical elements, viz. H, He, Li, Be, B, C, N and so forth. Certain combinations of these have significance so that we could call them words. We will, however, join the chemists and call them chemical formulae. These words, or chemical formulae, actually represent a property of a molecule, namely its atomic constitution. For instance, let us consider the set of all molecules with the chemical formula H_2O (i.e. all molecules which are represented by the word H_2O) and call this set $[H_2O]$. By definition, $[H_2O]=\{x;\ x$ has chemical formula $H_2O\}$. Similarly let $[H]=\{x;\ x$ has chemical formula $H\}$, and, $[O]=\{x;\ x$ has chemical formula $O\}$. Clearly, the property specified by these sets is the elemental content of the molecule. A better representation is achieved if the configuration of the molecule is also specified but we will not go into such detail here.

What can we say about the chemical equation

$$\text{(I)} \qquad 2H_2+O_2 \rightarrow 2H_2O?$$

Intuitively, it would appear that a molecule written as H_2 in the chemical language can be written as $<H, H>$ in the mathematical language. What then would $2H_2$ be in the mathematical language? Let us take it to be $<<H, H>, <H, H>>$ and denote the set of all such elements by $2[H]^2$, i.e. $2[H]^2=\{<<x, x>, <x, x>>;\ x$ has chemical formula $H\}$. Furthermore if we agree to translate $+$ of the chemical language into $\times$, the cartesian product in the mathematical language, then chemical reaction (I) may be represented by a function f, defined by

$$\text{(II)} \qquad f;\ (2[H]^2)\times[O]^2 \rightarrow [H_2O]^2$$

where $f(<<H, H>, <H, H>>, <O, O>) = <H_2O, H_2O>$.

The reverse chemical reaction is represented by the inverse of f, namely f^{-1} defined by

$$\text{(III)} \qquad f^{-1};\ [H_2O]^2 \rightarrow (2[H]^2)\times[O]^2$$

This manner of representing chemical reactions can sometimes be facilitated by using a more general cartesian product, namely $\prod_{i=1}^{n}$, defined for any integer n, by

$$\prod_{i=1}^{n} A_i = A_1 \times \ldots \times A_n$$

A sequence of chemical reactions can be written as a composition of functions. Given two functions $f{:}X \rightarrow Y$ and $g{:}\ Y \rightarrow Z$, the composition of f and g, written $f \circ g$ is defined by

$$f \circ g = \{<x, z>;\ x \varepsilon X_\wedge\ z \varepsilon Z_\wedge\ (\exists y \varepsilon Y)(y = f(\chi)_\wedge\ z = g(y))\}$$

or in short, $(f \circ g)(\chi) = g(f(\chi))$ for every χ in X. For instance, let f be the function in (II) and let $g = f^{-1}$. Then $f \circ f^{-1}$ is the identity function I having both as its domain, and range the set $(2[H]^2) \times [O]^2$, that is,

$$f \circ f^{-1} = I;\ (2[H]^2) \times [O]^2 \rightarrow (2[H]^2) \times [O]^2,$$

each molecule being mapped into itself. Clearly $f \circ g$ exists only if $D(g) \subseteq R(f)$. For arbitrary f and g, the existence of $f \circ g$ does not imply the existence of $g \circ f$ and even if both exist they need not be equal.

When one performs an experiment or produces a chemical, the molecules with which he deals are but a small fraction of the totality of all such molecules. For example, if, in chemical jargon, the product is H_2SO_4, then any one factory is producing a subset, say A, of $[H_2SO_4]$. Furthermore this event is taking place in time so that A depends on a time parameter t. Thus if we are producing H_2SO_4 in vat 2 of factory 1 then at any given time t we have $A(t) \subseteq [H_2SO_4]$ where $A(t) = \{x;\ x$ is a molecule with chemical formula H_2SO_4 at time t in vat number 2 of factory 1$\}$. We can incorporate this into the function representing the chemical reaction $H_2O + SO_3 \rightarrow H_2SO_4$ by letting T represent the interval of time during which the reaction takes place in vat 2 and by taking f to be,

$$f{:}\ [H_2O] \times [SO_3] \times T \rightarrow [H_2SO_4] \times T$$

whereby the point (x, y, t) for $x \varepsilon [H_2O]$, $y \varepsilon [SO_3]$ and $t \varepsilon T$ is mapped into the point (z, t), $z \varepsilon [H_2SO_4]$, meaning that at time t the molecule x of water and the molecule y of sulphur trioxide combine to produce a molecule of sulphuric acid.

Interest in the number of molecules of sulphuric acid produced in any given time period may lead one to consider sets of the form

(IV) $$B_a = \{<z, t>;\ z \varepsilon [H_2SO_4]_\wedge\ t \varepsilon [o, a) \subseteq T\}$$

where $[o, a)$ is the interval of time beginning with the initiation of the reaction, i.e. $t = o$, and ending almost at time a. The meaning of 'almost' intuitively is that for any time t_1 prior to a there is another time t_2 between t_1 and a. Symbolically this may be expressed

$$(\forall t_1)(t_1 < a \Rightarrow (\exists t_2)(t_1 < t_2 < a)).$$

Expression (IV) represents the set of all sulphuric acid molecules made within time a of the initiation of the reaction. If T, the interval of time required to complete the reaction (or bring it to equilibrium) is taken to be $[o, b)$, then B_a is a subset of B_b, i.e. $B_a \subseteq B_b$. We are in fact interested in all the *a priori* possible subsets of B_b. (During the course of any one production of sulphuric acid in vat 2 only certain subsets of B_b will actually be realized.) Denote by $\wp(B_b)$ the set of all the subsets of B_b. Let us define a function $\mu; \wp(B_b) \to N$, where N is the set of non-negative integers, by letting μ denote the number of sulphuric acid molecules in any given set B_a, i.e. for any B_a in $\wp(B_b)$, $\mu(B_a)$=the number of molecules in B_a. If the molecules of sulphuric acid are indistinguishable (as they will be if we ignore their kinetic energies, molecular energy states, etc.), two sets, B_{a1} and B_{a2}, may be considered to be equivalent if they have the same number of molecules, i.e.

$$B_{a1} \sim B_{a2} \Leftrightarrow \mu(B_{a1}) = \mu(B_{a2}) \tag{V}$$

We then say that B_{a1} and B_{a2} belong to the same equivalence class under the equivalence relation $\sim$. This equivalence class is denoted by either $B_{a1}/\sim$ or $B_{a2}/\sim$, both of which denote the same set. Under these circumstances, we say $\sim$ partitions B_b into equivalence classes and write, $B_b/\sim\ = \{B_a/\sim; a \varepsilon T\}$.

Why bother with all this? To answer this question let us take a quick look at the Kolmogorov formulation of probability theory.[(2)] Here we consider structures of the form $(\Omega, \mathcal{a}, P)$ where Ω is a set, $\mathcal{a}$ is σ-field of subsets of Ω, and P is a probability measure on $\mathcal{a}$. Sets and subsets are old hat. What are σ-fields? They are sets, which are closed under more general union and inter-section operations than $\cup$ and $\cap$ defined earlier as well as a third operation, called complementation. Closed means that the new sets formed by these operations are in $\mathcal{a}$ whenever the sets being united or intersected are in $\mathcal{a}$. A measure is a function whose domain consists of a σ-field of sets and which satisfies certain requirements, one of the requirements being with respect to the generalized union operation of the σ-field. A probability measure P is a measure such that $P(\Omega)=1$. This formulation of probability theory underlies much of the productive work in probability and statistics during the past thirty years. If we could put our chemical language into these terms then the two would in essence be one, at least as far as this type of problem is concerned.

To put our formulation in these terms we would have to show that $\wp(B_b/\sim)$ is closed under the operations of generalized (countable) union and complementation and hence is a σ-field. This we won't do. Also a probability measure would have to be defined on this σ-field. Under appropriate conditions, Bartholomay[(1.1)] has shown that for a chemical reaction represented by $f\colon A \times T \to B \times T$, the probability measure may be taken to be

$$P(A_t/\sim) = \binom{\mu(A_b)}{\mu(A_b) - \mu(A_t)} e^{-\mu(A_b) \cdot kt} (e^{kt} - 1)^{\mu(A_t)}$$

where k is the rate constant, and, t, A_t and $A_t/\sim$ are defined similar to the case for sulphuric acid formation with one difference: Bartholomay considers the chemical reactants rather than products. For further applications of this formulation to chemistry see Bartholomay,[1.2; 1.3] Kim,[3] and Bharucha-Reid.[4] For similar formulations in the fields of physiology, bacteriology and neurophysiology see Martin,[5] Mode,[6] and Bernhard,[7] respectively.

This example of expressing chemistry in the language of mathematics was of necessity sketchy. It can be seen, however, that there is a natural relationship between the languages of mathematics and chemistry. It is my contention that the languages of all the other technologies share this relationship.

To strengthen this contention let us take a glance at the biological sciences. Although biologists themselves have not as yet familiarized themselves with this language, theroetical biophysicists, such as N. Rashevsky[8] and R. Rosen,[9] have made significant progress in using it to describe biological phenomena. For instance, R. Rosen[9.1] has introduced the notion of (M, R) systems where M is a set consisting of components of the biological system, and R is a set consisting essentially of relations between the outputs of these components and the components themselves. With this sort of formulation he has, for example, given a descriptive definition of reproduction as follows:[9.2] Suppose, for simplicity, that M consists of the single map $f\colon A \to B$ and that R consists of a map $\Phi_f\colon B \to H(A, B)$ where $H(A, B) = \{g\colon g$ is a function with domain A and range $B\}$. Then, we say f has been reproduced if there is an $a \varepsilon A$ such that $\Phi_f(f(a)) = f$. Biologists have not, however, taken to Rosen's work not so much because of his unpoetic description of reproduction but rather because of the existing language barrier. The terminology frequented in Rosen's papers, of course, is that of mathematics, as introduced in this discourse, whereas biologists, although obviously dealing with the same notions, express these notions in a different tongue.

In summary: the sciences have sprung from man's ability to reason and so this serves as their common ground. Man's reasoning, however, has been expressed in various languages and these have kept their associated technologies apart. A common language is therefore needed. The objective of this discussion was to present the language of mathematics as a suitable candidate for this position, which is essentially the position of first violinist in the orchestra of science. I trust that the vagueness inherent in this discourse has served only to enhance this candidacy.

REFERENCES

1. BARTHOLOMAY, A.
   (1.1) Molecular Set Theory: A Mathematical Representation for Chemical Reaction Mechanisms. *Bull. math. Biophys.* **22** (1960), 285–307.
   (1.2) A Stochastic Approach to Statistical Kinetics with Application to Enzyme Kinetics: *Biochem.* **1**, 2 (March, 1962), 223–30.
   (1.3) The General Catalytic Queue Process: in, *Stochastic Models in Medicine and Biology*. John Gurland (Editor), University of Wisconsin Press (1964).
2. LOEVE, M. *Probability Theory*. Van Nostrand, 1963, p. 150.
3. KIM, S. K. Mean First Passage Time for a Random Walker and its Application to Chemical Kinetics: *J. chem. Phys.* **28**, 6 (June 1958), 1057–67.
4. BHARUCHA-REID, A. T. *Elements of the Theory of Markov Processes and Their Applications*. McGraw-Hill, 1960, 359–73.
5. MARTIN, L. Stochastic Processes in Physiology: *in The Fourth Berkeley Symposium, on Probability and Statistics*, Vol. IV, J. Neyman, 1961, 307–20.
6. MODE, C. J. A Stochastic Model of the Dynamics of Host-Pathogen Systems with Mutation. *Bull. math. Biophys.* **26** (1964), 205–33.
7. BERNHARD, R. Towards a Chemical Kinetic Brain Model. *J. Theor. Biol.* **6**, 244 (1964), 158–73.
8. RASHEVSKY, N. Abstract Mathematical Molecular Biology, *Bull. math. Biophys.* **23** (1961), 237–60.
9. ROSEN, R.
   (9.1) A Relational Theory of Biological Systems, *Bull. math. Biophys.* **20** (1958), 245–60.
   (9.2) A Relational Theory of the Structural Changes Induced in Biological Systems by Alterations in Environment. *Bull. math. Biophys.* **23** (1961), 165–71.

13

PROFESSOR ARNOLD REISMAN

The Analysis and Synthesis of Production and Operations Systems: An Analytical Approach Bridging All Technologies

The rapid development of new analytic tools deriving from mathematics, physical science, economics and engineering, and the advent of high-speed computing machinery, both analogue and digital, has made many heretofore formidable problems manageable. Solutions can now be obtained with speed and economy, to the mathematical formulation of problems which in yesteryear were either not tackled at all, relegated to the laboratory or treated by rule-of-thumb methods.

The great strides made within the last decades in the development of technology and of technologists have introduced a new level of conceptual complexity and hence developed a great need for technical specialists. This new need for specialization is superimposed on the traditional lines of professional demarcation. Thus, characteristic of the approach to the solution of technical and especially of management problems in today's industry, commerce, public and private institutions is the consideration of many independently conceived problem areas. Professional people address themselves strictly to those questions which have been traditionally within the province of their own discipline. Generally, such categorization of problems fits into the conventional functional compartmentalization of enterprises such as research, design, production, finance, marketing and others. Moreover, within the compartments listed there are additional specialties and subspecialties. Thus within the design category we have electrical, mechanical, civil, etc., engineers each having limited interests in the work of their colleagues outside the functional group. We are all familiar with the differences in terminology and approaches to problem solution between accountants and research scientists, marketing people and design engineers. Customarily each deals with only a specific segment of the enterprise, attempting to perfect only that for which he is held responsible.

The complexity of military decisions facing the Allied general staffs during the second world war has ushered in a new era: the era of interdisciplinary scientific attacks on complex problems. The field of Operations Research, though having roots in the work of Charles Babbage and Frederick W. Taylor, was born. Operations Research has in turn rejuvenated the scientific approach in many disciplines, especially in management and industrial engineering. It has given birth to many new techniques on its own and was quick to exploit new methodologies developed in other areas. It made great inroads into the operations of the military establishment and is also making its weight felt in industry. However, because of their need for rigour and preoccupation with exact and/or optimum solutions, Operations Research practitioners and theorists, too, have tended to tackle lesser problems than those which can be handled with existing hardware and software.

Recent activity directed towards the solution of business or industrial problems can conceptually be broken down into the dichotomy of optimizing and non-optimizing methods. Optimizing techniques are those which purport to find the very best way to operate the system. This is generally done by abstracting the reality into a set of mathematical relations between the exogeneous variables which drive the system, the variables which determine the system behaviour and the criteria functions which judge the system's output and or behaviour. The equations are then mathematically manipulated to determine the conditions that will maximize (or minimize) the criteria. A common example of this technique is linear programming. In this case the allocation of scarce resources is modelled by a set of linear equations representing the restrictions on resource allocation. Subject to these restrictions an objective equation, representing the value of any allocation, is maximized. Where there are several dependent variables to be optimized or where the model is non-linear, optimization is generally ruled out, though there are ingenious techniques for solving non-linear problems under special conditions.

Most socio-economic and physical systems are described by non-linear relationships, which along with the extreme complexities involved in their mathematical description, generally rule out optimization techniques. Not only are non-linearity and feedback vexing problems for model builders in this domain, but there are added difficulties encountered. Comparative weighting of variables where more than one criterion is involved in the optimization is one of these. Another is that of deciding upon the criteria when dealing with stochastic processes—

should the expected value be used or the expected value and the second moment, etc.?

Non-maximizing methods are subject to these same problems; however, one of them can handle the problem of non-linearity quite readily. This is the technique of simulation. Simulation requires first a mathematical model or analogue of the system relating the appropriate variables in such a manner that the state of the system at any point in time may be determined. The model is manipulated so as to generate a sequential history, at appropriate time intervals, of the states of the system. In this fashion, then, a representative history of the system is created and it is from this history that we infer system characteristics. The purpose of simulation is to duplicate the essence of a system so that we may evaluate proposed design, determine the operating characteristics of a system under new or changed stimuli, compare the efficiencies of alternate designs, etc. Simulation, both digital and analogue, has been conducted on a grand scale. The advent of high-speed digital computers has materially enhanced the attractiveness of this tool, so much so, in fact, that computers can reduce man months of manual simulation to machine seconds for an equivalent amount of work. Added assistance in programming simulators for computers has been introduced by compiler languages such as Simscript, Dynamo and GPSS.

It is readily recognized that computer simulation is a technique which is not limited to applications in any one discipline. Moreover it is not limited to any one discipline in any given application. Systems simultaneously involving electrical, mechanical, social, economic, etc., phenomena can be thus studied. However, in order to study the dynamics of such complex systems one needs to have a conceptual, structural and a mathematical framework within which to operate, as well as a breed of technologists who can and will consider all of the factors affecting the system under study. This paper describes a generalized model for production and operations systems—a framework for systems studies. This model was recently developed by this author as part of his doctoral dissertation.

Production or operations systems are considered to encompass the workings of factories, offices, hospitals; chemical, process or power plants; supermarkets, educational institutions, etc. Production is a process by which goods and/or services are created. Although the word 'goods' in this context is no different from common usage, the word 'services' takes on a more broad interpretation. Services range anywhere from the heat treatment of machine parts to the design of engineering systems. The word 'service' in this context also incorporates transformations performed on matter, energy, information, people or populations, capital equipment and monies. The design and control of systems producing goods or services is an area with which this paper is concerned.

A generalized descriptive model of production or operations systems

In line with the thinking expressed above, a model of a production or operations system will be described next. According to the stated definition, a refinery, a design office, a hospital or supermarket all represent special cases which have special characteristics. The model presented here has inputs which represent the flow of materials, energy, paper-work forms, and the customers or patients, as the case may be. The inputs to this system will be processed in some way by a series of operations; the sequence of operations and the number thereof are specified for each input. For any given input, the operations may vary both in number and in kind.

The characteristics of the operations performed may vary from purely mechanical, electrical, thermal and/or chemical, assembly, to inspection and control, receiving, dispatching to subsequent operation, shipping, personal confrontation such as a conference or an interview, memoranda, etc. The outputs from an operation system can take the form of any number of chemical products, as is the case in a petroleum refinery; completed manufactured items; products of a processing plant; healed patients, as is the case in hospitals; software as is the case in research and/or development organizations, etc. The model provides for temporary storage of the various flows within the system, it provides for generation of flows, i.e. sources, and for the final disappearance of flows, i.e. the sinks. The flows are transported within the system between all operations through any number of the common methods. Thus, flows of fluids can be conveyed through closed or open conduits, the flow of electricity can be conveyed through electrical transmission lines, heat through heat conductors, information through oral or written communications, rigid bodies through conveyor belts, etc., and people such as patients, clients or customers, through self-transportation. Information is sensed at various operating points of this system, and also in its surroundings. It is conveyed by any of the means commonly used through the information gathering and processing system, from whence it is transmitted to the decision function and back through the controlling elements of the various operations.

Structural framework

The basic schematic diagram of the production system is shown in Fig. 1. This is a highly aggregated diagram, both in terms of flows and in terms of operations. Yet it shows the major flow paths and the major places where transformations take place.

The flows, as indicated on the diagram, are of six distinct types. The dashed line with circles represents orders flow. It can be seen that the orders originate in the surroundings of the system studied. They may be purely exogeneous inputs to the system or responses from the external world to information emanating from the system. In general, these orders are time-dependent. Quite often they can be considered to flow continuously or quasicontinuously. However, there is nothing in this model which precludes discrete or even stochastic flows. These orders enter the system through the Professional and/or Service Function. This is the intelligence arm of the model. It corresponds to the Admissions and Counselling Office in the case of educational institutions, and to the engineering staffs of manufacturing organizations.

Based upon decisions made in this function, the incoming orders may be either routed to a sink, i.e. 'filed', or, after certain transformations, be sent on to either the Operations Function, the Inventory, or the Proposals and/or Sales Function. If the order is for proposals, then it is routed to the Proposals and/or Sales group, from which a proposal in the form of information (dashed line) is sent out. On the other hand, if the order is for goods, services or energy which cannot be filled from inventory, then the Operations Functions fulfils the orders through production. If, however, the decision is made to fill the order from inventory, then it is thus routed and filled. Now, in the case where orders are sent to Operations, the intelligence arm or Professional and/or Service Function must satisfy Operations with the necessary labour[1] materials, energy equipment and external services, all at the right time and of the right kind. Thus, information must be sent through the Employment, Financial and/or Ordering Policies so that orders may go out to the various pools. Upon receipt of an order, the labour pool routes people into the system (double solid line). The populations enter through the Training[2] sections where they are processed and sent on to either Operations or, perhaps, the Professional Function itself.

[1]Labour, as referred to here, may be highly professional, as in the case in hospitals or universities.

[2]The Training, Processing Delay for Materials and Energy or for Equipment may, for expediency, be used to include some of the response characteristics of the pools.

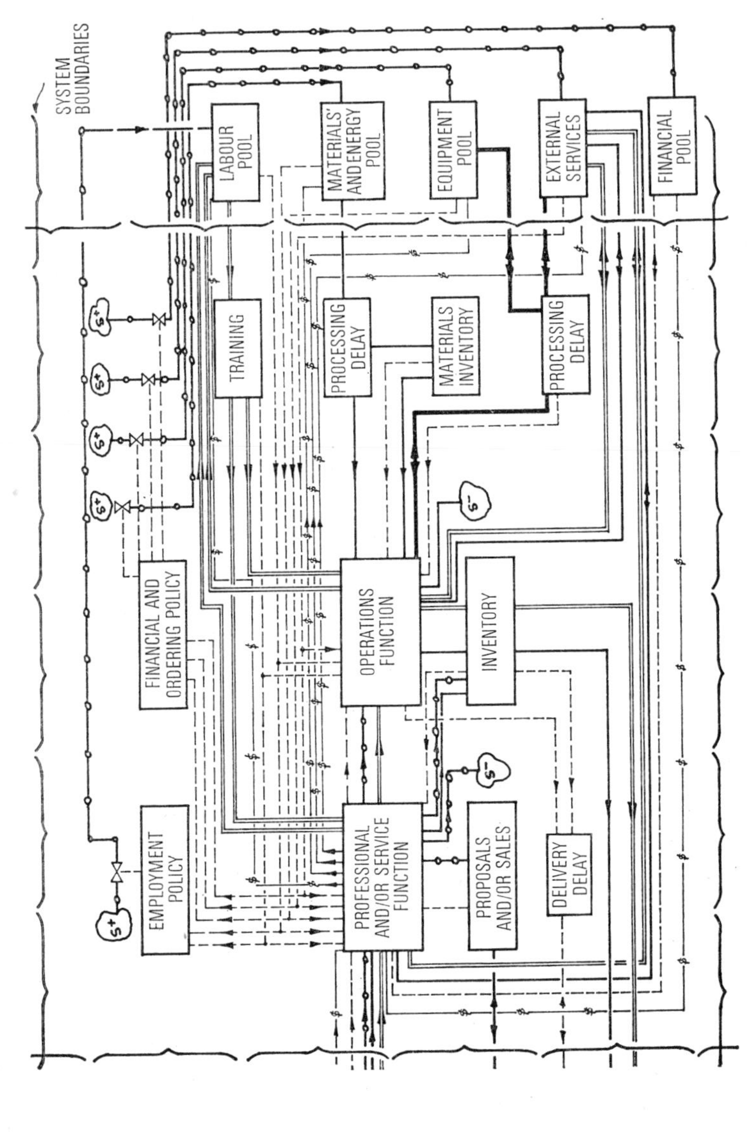

The General Model Schematic

– – –	Information Flow	—$—	Cash Flow	(S+)	Source
—o—	Orders' Flow	═	Populations' Flow	X	Control Valve
——	Materials' or Energy Flow	▬	Capital Equipment Flow	(S−)	Sink

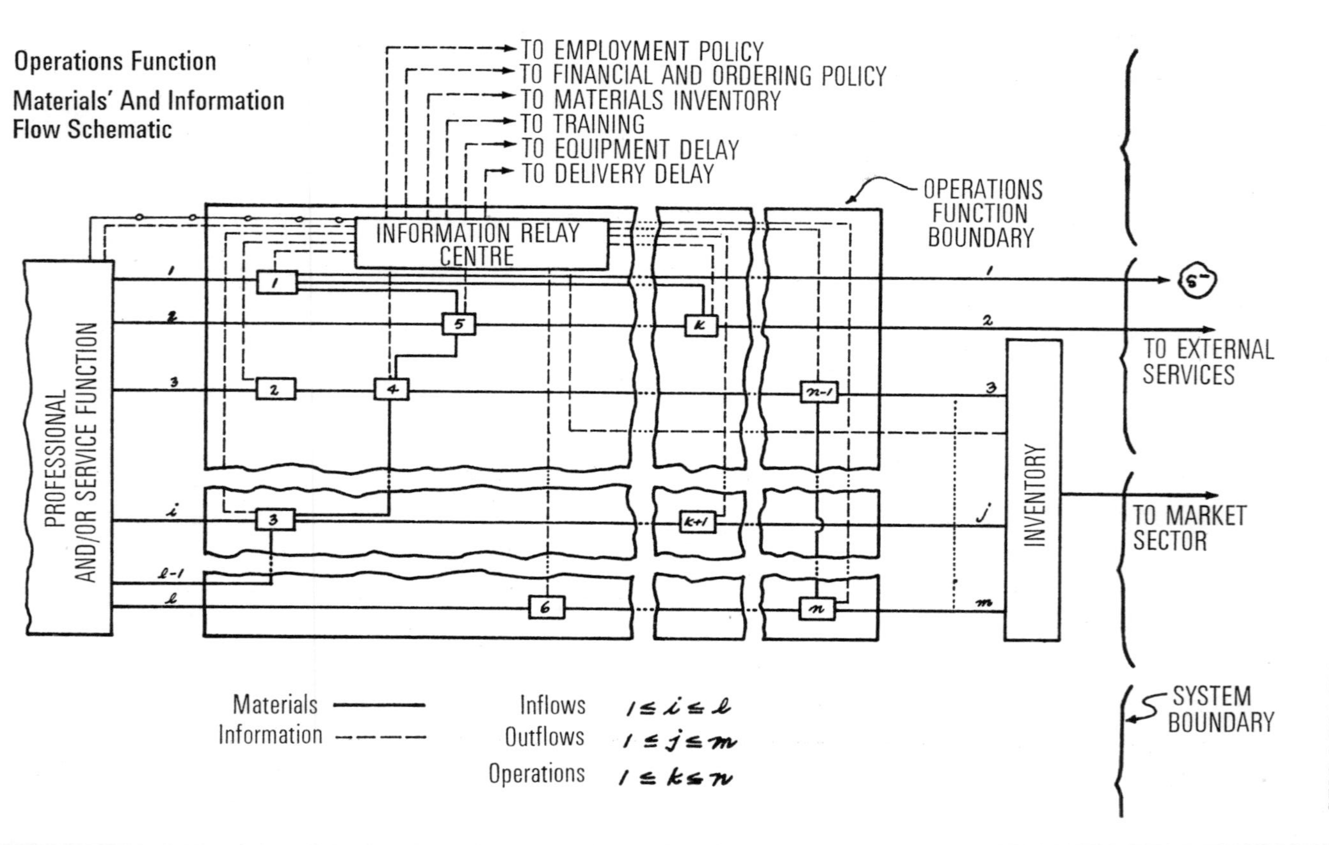

Operations Function
Materials' And Information Flow Schematic

Operations Function
Materials' Flow Schematic

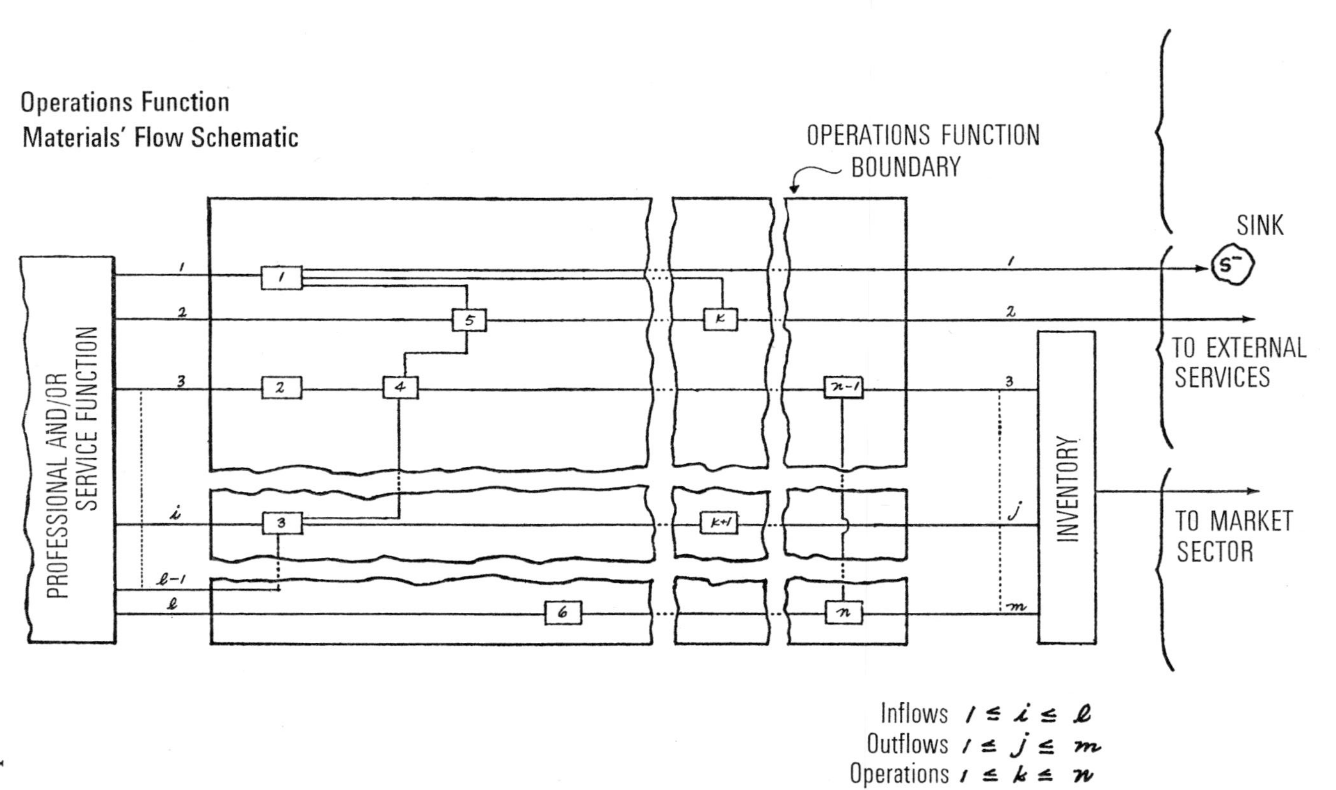

Similarly, the Materials and Energy Pool will route its resources to the system through the Processing Delay from where they may be sent on to either the Materials Inventory or to the Operations Function directly. The Equipment Pool will send capital equipment (solid wide line) into its processing delay and on to Operations. The External Services Pool performs as the name implies—services which cannot, due to the lack of capability, capacity limitations, etc., be performed internally to the system.

In the case of manufactured metal parts, this may be heat treating or any of the specialized metallurgical or chemical processes. In the case of a hospital, this may be radiological treatment for patients, equipment overhaul or specialized training for physicians. The Financial Pool represents the banks or the investment sector of the economy. This is the originating point for all external financing. It provides the necessary make-up capital for the system, while, at the same time, being the place whereto surplus cash goes (dashed line with dollar signs). Of course, cash also enters the system from the general environment in payment for goods produced or services rendered, and, for similar reasons, leaves the system to the various pools. It should be noticed that there is no flow of cash between segments of the system, i.e. internally. This is reasonable. Manufacturing does not ever pay in cash or even by cheque for materials coming from inplant materials inventory. These transactions are covered by intraplant flows of information.

Information flows may be of several kinds. They may be in the form of reports or memoranda, i.e. written communications, yet they may be verbal as well. They may be requests for further information or they may be commands or instructions. In addition to the above, information flows may contain the routine data from Operations, Inventory Delivery or from Processing Delays. Information flows, as discussed later, may exhibit all of the characteristics of physical flows, i.e. information may be generated, stored, transduced, dissipated, and its flows may exhibit inertia. Goods or energy may enter the production system from the general surroundings in addition to the materials and energy pool. The flows from the general surroundings may be seen to first enter the Professional and/or Service Function. Here intelligence operations are performed upon them, and they are routed to either Operations or Inventory, depending on need.

The highly aggregated function blocks, as well as flows, of Fig. 1 may be broken down to any level of aggregation desired and for each type flow, through schematics such as the one represented for Materials, flows through the Operations Function, i.e. Fig. 2. Within the Operations Function boundary, each small block represents either a transformation (physical, chemical, etc.) or a flow element such as resistance, inertance, capacitance, etc. In addition, these small blocks may represent sources, sinks or any combination of the factors mentioned.

The interconnexion of all pertinent diagrams such as Figs. 2 and 3, according to the structure embodied within Fig. 1, represents for any given system the equivalent network. Such a network is next analysed according to the mathematical model which follows. In certain cases, the network, once drawn, may be directly simulated on special purpose computers. General purpose computers may also, under certain conditions, be used for direct simulation.

MATHEMATICAL FRAMEWORK

Problem formulation

It is possible to make a fairly clear-cut distinction between basic physical, social or economic processes and complex socio-economic and/or engineering systems. In the former, isolation is both assumed and established; and the problems are concerned chiefly with the ascertainment of predictive relationships between significant variables. In the socio-economic and/or engineering situation, on the other hand, interconnexion of primitive components is essential, the problems being concerned with overall system behaviour given a set of specific components.

In either case, from the abstract point of view, one is confronted with a 'system' in which generally a multiplicity of observed variables Y_i is at least assumed to be related to another multiplicity of known or unknown variables X_k. The first multiplicity we can think of as the 'output vector' $\bar{Y}$ and the second group as the input vector $\bar{X}$. Thus, the functional dependency may be expressed as

$$\bar{Y} = \psi(\bar{X})$$

where ψ, in general, is non-linear. Historically, the $\bar{X}$ quantities have also been called 'independent' or 'exogenous' variables and, by contrast, the $\bar{Y}$ quantities the 'dependent' or 'endogeneous' variables. Besides these $\bar{X}$ and $\bar{Y}$ quantities, a socioeconomic system, as well as any physical system, is also generally described by means of its 'geometry' or 'structural parameters' and by its 'properties' or 'material parameters'. The foregoing characteristic quantities may be arranged usefully in a table as follows:

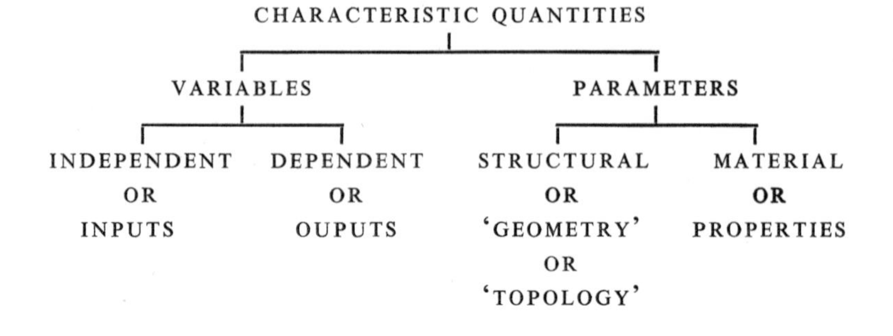

These characteristic quantities are related, through sets of equations such as those written at the nodes or junctions and those written across branches and through an interweaving sub-model with which the advisability of proceeding with a certain policy can be evaluated from the financial point of view.

Derivations of the mathematical framework

This sub-model has two parts. The first part develops a set of k node or junction equations for any network having $k+1$ junctions,[3] a junction being defined as any point in the system at which three[4] or more flows take place. These equations are merely expressions of conservation at the junction of the flow variable in question. The expressions recognize that, in general, any junction may possess o storage capacities,[5] p sinks,[6] q sources,[7] and that any one junction i may be connected to B others, which means that there are B flows at the junction i. The set of equations (1) is presented on page 134. Some of the terms, though defined on that page, need further explanation:

[3]The $k+1$ junctions discussed in this and the subsequent section should not be confused with the fact that Figs. 2 and 3 show n branches inasmuch as Figs. 2 and 3 represent sub-systems, and the $k+1$ referred to here represents the number of branches in the total network.

[4]Any source, sink, or storage rate at a junction may be considered a 'flow' for the purposes of this definition. Example: a point in the network having but one flow in and one flow out is not a junction, but if it, in addition, has at least one storage, sink or source element and under same conditions a transducer, then it is a junction.

[5]The letter o as used here is not zero—it represents the number of different storage capacities at the junction.

[6]A 'sink' is an infinitely large 'dump' for the flow variable in question.

[7]A 'source' is an infinitely large 'mine' for the flow variable in question.

W The flow variable represents the rate of throughput. It may be in units of goods, services, information, etc., all per unit of time.

V The capacity parameter represents an 'area' which, when multiplied by Z, the 'level', produces a 'volume' stored. Thus V may represent the floor space of a warehouse; if Z respectively represents the height relative to the floor to which the goods are stored, then the product VZ is the storage volume and the product $V(dZ/dt)$ is the rate at which the flow variable (the goods in this example) get stored.

Z The level—see explanation for V.

S^- The sink rate represents the rate at which the flow variable forever disappears.

S^+ The source rate represents the rate at which material is being created by removing it from a virtually inexhaustible 'mine'.

$\bar{x}$ The pertinent vector represents any parameter or set of parameters upon which the variable in question may depend. Example: the rate of change of Z may depend upon its instantaneous position within the storage volume.

Equations (1) represent node or junction relations. It should be noted that the number of independent node equations one can write for any system is one less[8] than the number of independent nodes.

NODE OR JUNCTION EQUATIONS

Net Rate of Flow at a Juntion =

Σ Rates of Flow into the Juntion −

Σ Rates of Flow out of the Junction = −

Σ Losses to Sinks within the Junction +

Σ Gains from Sources at a Junction +

Σ Rates of Accumulation at a Junction

[8]This is true for all simply connected networks. For networks involving mutual inductances or their analogues, whatever they may be, see Weinberg, L. *Network Analysis and Synthesis*, McGraw Hill, New York, 1962.

Assuming that the i-th junction has B junctions directly connected to it then:

$$\sum_B W_{1B} = \left[\sum_o V_o \frac{dZ_o(t,\bar{x}_o)}{dt} - \sum_p S_p^-(t,\bar{x}_p) + \sum_q S_q^+(t,\bar{x}_q)\right]_{1B}$$

$$\vdots$$

$$\sum_B W_{iB} = \left[\sum_o V_o \frac{dZ_o(t,\bar{x})}{dt} - \sum_p S_p^-(t,\bar{x}_p) + \sum_q S_q^+(t,\bar{x}_q)\right]_{iB} \quad \ldots\ldots\ldots\ldots \quad (1)$$

$$\vdots$$

$$\sum_B W_{AB} = \left[\sum_o V_o \frac{dZ_o(t,\bar{x}_o)}{dt} - \sum_p S_p^-(t,\bar{x}_p) + \sum_q S^+_q(t,\bar{x}_q)\right]_{AB}$$

Where: W = The Flow Variable t = Time
V = The Capacity Parameter
Z = A Level
S^- = A Sink Rate S^+ = A Source Rate
$\bar{x}$ = Some Pertinent Vector

Note: $W_{AB} = -W_{BA}$ This is not an independent equation.

Equations (2) represent potential or branch equations. A potential equation can be written for each of the m branches interconnecting the $k+1$ nodes.

These equations are expressions of the potential or force balances between the two terminal points of the branch, i.e. the two nodes which are interconnected by the branch in question. The equations state that the potential difference $P_{ij}(t)$ for any branch is equal to the difference in potential $H_i(t) - H_j(t)$ between node i and node j, which in turn is equal to the sum of the potential drops across all impedances and transducers[9] which are in series connected along the branch. The three types

[9]The 'potential drop' may be at times negative across a transducer. This is, in fact, the case across pumps, batteries, amplifiers of all sorts, etc.

BRANCH OR POTENTIAL EQUATIONS

$$P_{12}(t) = [H_1(t)-H_2(t)] = \left[\sum_j I_j(W_{12},t)\frac{dW_{12}(t,\bar{x}_j)}{dt} + \sum_k \int_{t_1}^{t_2} \frac{W_{12}(t,\bar{x}_k)dt}{C(W_{12},t)_k} + \sum_i R_i(W_{12},t)W_{12}(t,\bar{x}_i) + \sum_l \Delta P_l\right]_{12}$$

$$P_{13}(t) = [H_1(t)-H_3(t)] = \left[\sum_j I_j(W_{13},t)\frac{dW_{13}(t,\bar{x})}{dt} + \sum_k \int_{t_1}^{t_2} \frac{W_{13}(t,\bar{x}_k)dt}{C(W_{13},t)_k} + \sum_i R_i(W_{13},t)W_{13}(t,\bar{x}_i) + \sum_l \Delta P_l\right]_{13}$$

$$\vdots \qquad\qquad \vdots \qquad \vdots \qquad\qquad \vdots \qquad\qquad \vdots \qquad\qquad \vdots \quad \ldots\ldots\ldots\ldots\ldots\ldots (2)$$

$$P_{1B}(t) = [H_1(t)-H_B(t)] = \left[\sum_j I_j(W_{1B},t)\frac{dW_{1B}(t,\bar{x}_j)}{dt} + \sum_k \int_{t_1}^{t_2} \frac{W_{1B}(t,\bar{x}_k)dt}{C(W_{1B},t)_k} + \sum_i R_i(W_{1B},t)W_{1B}(t,\bar{x}_i) + \sum_l \Delta P_l\right]_{1B}$$

$P_{21} = -P_{12}$ This is not an independent equation. $P_{22} = 0$ The potential difference at a point is 0.

$$P_{23}(t) = [H_2(t)-H_3(t)] = \left[\sum_j I_j(W_{23},t)\frac{dW_{23}(t,\bar{x}_j)}{dt} + \sum_k \int_{t_1}^{t_2} \frac{W_{23}(t,\bar{x}_k)dt}{C(W_{23},t)} + \sum_i R_i(W_{23},t)W_{23}(t,\bar{x}_i) + \sum_l \Delta P_l\right]_{23}$$

$$\vdots \qquad\qquad \vdots \qquad \vdots \qquad\qquad \vdots \qquad\qquad \vdots \qquad\qquad \vdots$$

$$P_{2B}(t) = [H_2(t)-H_B(t)] = \left[\sum_j I_j(W_{2B},t)\frac{dW_{2B}(t,\bar{x}_j)}{dt} + \sum_k \int_{t_1}^{t_2} \frac{W_{2B}(t,\bar{x}_k)dt}{C(W_{2B},t)_k} + \sum_i R_i(W_{2B},t)W_{2B}(t,\bar{x}_i) + \sum_l \Delta P_l\right]_{2B}$$

$$\vdots \qquad\qquad \vdots \qquad \vdots \qquad\qquad \vdots \qquad\qquad \vdots \qquad\qquad \vdots$$

$$PA_1(t) = [H_A(t)-H_1(t)] = \left[\sum_j I_j(W_{A1},t)\frac{dW_{A1}(t,\bar{x}_j)}{dt} + \sum_k \int_{t_1}^{t_2} \frac{W_{A1}(t,\bar{x}_k)dt}{C(W_{A1},t)_k} + \sum_i R_i(W_{A1},t)W_{A1}(t,\bar{x}_i) + \sum_l \Delta P_l\right]_{A1}$$

$$\vdots \qquad\qquad \vdots \qquad \vdots \qquad\qquad \vdots \qquad\qquad \vdots \qquad\qquad \vdots$$

$$P_{AB}(t) = [\mathrm{H}_A(t)-H_B(t)] = \left[\sum_j I_j(W_{AB},t)\frac{dW_{AB}(t\bar{x}_j)}{dt} + \sum_k \int_{t_1}^{t_2} \frac{W_{AB}(t,\bar{x}_k)dt}{C(W_{AB},t)_k} + \sum_i R_i(W_{AB},t)W_{AB}(t,\bar{x}_i) + \sum_l \Delta P_l\right]_{AB}$$

Where:
P_{AB} = Potential Difference between nodes A and B
R = Resistance or Dissipation parameter
L = Inertia parameter
C = Capacitance parameter
ΔP = Transducer potential difference parameter
H = Potential at a node

of impedances to flow[10] for physical, psychological or economic transformations are discussed, from the quantitative point of view, in the dissertation cited earlier.[11] Here the general mathematical formulation of the potential drop due to such impedances will be considered.

Resistance R

In general, the resistance element may be a non-linear device which may be a function[12] of the flow rate, of time and of some other vector $\bar{x}_i$. It is recognized that the flow rate is itself a function of time and of the vector $\bar{x}$ which may represent position. However, R may be a function of time independent of the time dependency of W. Such is, in fact, the case during the transient period describing the learning or, on the other hand, fatigued stage of a human being transmitting information. The instantaneous product of the resistance parameter and flow variable, i.e. $R_i(W_{jk},t,\bar{x}_i)W_{jk}(t,\bar{x}_i)$ yields the instantaneous potential drop across the resistance element R_i.

Capacitance C

In general, the capacitance element is, too, a function of time, the flow variable and some other vector $\bar{x}$. The $\bar{x}$ dependence is illustrated by the case of non-cylindrical surge tanks, i.e. funnel-shaped fluid storage basins. The time dependence of C, independent of the functional time dependency of W, may be illustrated by the case of a basin whose walls recede with time, or by the case of a capacitor-type level or thickness gage whose operation, and therefore worth, depends on the fact that the space between two surfaces, and consequently the capacitance, change with time. We have shown earlier that if V is the 'floor space' of a warehouse and Z the level to which goods are stored, the term $V(dZ/dt)$ is the rate of storage. In integral formulation, the height or the potential of the stored variable is given $Z=\int(1/V)dt$ where V in this example is equivalent to the capacitance parameter C_k. If the walls of the storage basin are not vertical then $V=C_k(Z)$, that is, the capacitance parameter

[10]Admittance being the reciprocals of impedances.

[11]Arnold Reisman, 'A General Model for Production Systems', Ph.D. Dissertation, Department of Engineering, University of California, Los Angeles, June 1963. Available through the Los Angeles and Berkeley Libraries of the University of California and through University Microfilms, Ann Arbor, Michigan, *and* Arnold Reisman & E. S. Buffa, 'A General Model for Production and Operations Systems'. *Management Science* **11**, 64–79, September 1964. Also, Reprint No. 23, Western Management Science Institute, University of California, Los Angeles.

[12]Due to space limitations, R_i, I_j and C_k were not shown to be functions of the respective $\bar{x}$'s in the equations.

is a function of the height to which the stored variable has risen. In this case again Z in $V=C_k(Z)$ takes the place of the generalized variable $\bar{x}$. Similarly, if the walls of the basin recede with time, then $V=C_k(t)$, and if both effects are operative then $V=C_k(t,Z)$, etc. The time integral of the ratio of the flow variable and capacitance parameter, i.e.
$\int_{t_1}^{t_2} (W_{ij}(t,\bar{x}_k)/C_k(W_{ij},t,\bar{x}_k))\ dt$ yields the instantaneous potential drop across the capacitance element C.

Inertance I

The inertance, just as resistance and capacitance, may, in general, be a function of W, t and $\bar{x}$. Goods distribution pipelines exhibit inertance. Typically, the consumer cannot take possession of a product at the instant it leaves the factory. Similarly, a distributor cannot instantaneously stop the flow of goods in transit. The time-delays in both instances are due to inertance. The product of the inertia parameter and the time-rate of change of the flow variable, i.e.
$I_i(W_{ik},t,\bar{x})(dW_{ik}(t,\bar{x}_t)/dt)$ yields the potential drop across an inductive element.

Transducers ΔP

Transducers transform energy, matter, information, etc., from one form to another. They are, in general,[13] functions of time, flow or throughput, and the vector $\bar{x}$. The flow dependence is well established in the case of pumps, compressors and turbines. Here the 'characteristic' curve provides the dependence of the 'head' or pressure upon flow. These devices may also be used to illustrate time dependence, i.e. the transient behaviour following start-up or shut-down. As pertains the vector $\bar{x}$, the effectiveness of these devices is often dependent upon altitude at which they are operated. Airborne gas turbines and their associated compressors certainly bear out the above.

In the area of communication, the human being referred to earlier exhibits transient behaviour during the learning stages of information or, for that matter, matter transformations. His 'characteristic' curves are definitely throughput dependent and often displaced or altered when the environment in which the operation takes place is changed. The term ΔP, in a very condensed fashion, indicates the potential drop or gain across a transducer.

[13]Due to space limitations, the given equations do not specify these dependencies.

It should be noted that there are as many independent branch equations as there are independent branches and that all of them must be used in conjunction with the independent node equations in order to completely analyse the problem.

Concluding remarks

The model described in this paper is now being refined. It is already being applied to studies concerned with the operations of: a school of higher learning, a large chemical processing enterprise, a hospital and a national agency charged with the regulation of energy resources exploitation within the country. The dissertation cited showed how purely physical systems can be considered special cases of this model. In fact, previous simulations by this author of heat transfer networks, and complex hydraulic systems, were used as a basis for generalization in the development of this model. Thus, presented here was an approach to problem solution knowing no disciplinary boundaries.

14

LESLIE HOLLIDAY

Interaction of Technologies

Specialization increases inexorably in the world of technology. In the Stone Age there were no specialists and every man in the tribe was fully trained to carry out the laborious tasks which were necessary to keep him alive. Every man was concerned with the problems of food, of defence, of shelter, and with the straightforward issue of survival. Specialization began at the time of the neolithic revolution in the Middle East, when farming began and urban communities sprang up. This was accompanied by the emergence of craftsmen—of potters, weavers, smiths and farmers. It had taken about one million years for specialization to begin.

Within the space of about ten thousand years, we have reached the stage of specialization in technology at which we operate today. We have brick technologists who know nothing about plastics; we have plastics technologists who know nothing about metals; we have metals technologists who know nothing about wood; we have wood technologists who know nothing about textiles, and so it goes on. This is an exaggeration, of course, but it is the pattern which seems to be emerging. Can we therefore look forward to a time when we have specialization in low-density polyethylene of density 0.925, or of polyurethane foams made from polypropylene glycols? If this were to happen, progress would slow down because communication between technologists would be further impeded, and technologists would be trying to solve an increasing number of problems with unsuitable raw materials. Quite apart from this, to attempt to organize the field of technology into broader disciplines represents a fascinating intellectual challenge.

If we step aside and look at the field of science for a moment, the situation is quite different. The human mind has an urge to understand the external world, and to produce order and system out of facts. The scientist wants above all to produce statements and laws of the widest possible validity. A consequence of this is that a coherent and interrelated structure has been built up in the sciences. It is true that, viewed from Olympus, the realm of science would seem to be a continuum, and the branches of physical and biological science would appear to merge into one another and would seem to extend into further fields of knowledge and activity such as mathematics, philosophy, psychology and so on. However, even though the boundaries which exist between the sciences are arbitrary, there is an order and a system in science which is lacking in technology.

Problems of technology

One of the first problems in technology is a problem in semantics. The word 'technology' is of necessity vague, since it embraces a vast span of interests and activities. If we qualify it in some way, for example, by saying polymer technology, we immediately describe a subject with certain boundaries. These boundaries may then become restrictive and artificial. Technology is, in fact, the science of industry, and comprises the application of science and of scientific method to industry. The classical way in which technology has been subdivided has been to group together industrial activities, using as a key certain commercial and technical interests which they have in common. Thus we talk of space technology, glass technology, petroleum technology and of many others. This is the first stage of evolution of technology, and represents a major step forward, since it stimulates the internal development of each particular technology. It does not necessarily, however, lead to the stimulation of one technology by another, which is the second stage of technological evolution. If technologists are to advance more rapidly as the result of mutual interaction, it is necessary that technology should be subdivided differently and reorganized so that the maximum number of fundamental similarities emerge.

This need becomes even more obvious when one examines the list of research associations in receipt of Government grants. This includes those listed opposite.

To what extent can one achieve a synthesis with these pieces? If they are part of a jigsaw puzzle, how can one best produce a recognizable picture? We need today someone to do for the evolution of technologies what Mendeléeff and Darwin did a hundred years ago for the growth of chemistry and biology. This raises the question:

Who is responsible for producing order out of the chaos which exists in the field of technology, and who is to perceive the technological skeins which run through industry?

ASSOCIATIONS IN RECEIPT OF GOVERNMENT GRANTS[1]

Baking	Gelatine and Glue	Paint
Brush	Glass	Paper
Cast Iron	Heating	Printing
Coke	Hosiery	Rubber and Plastics
Cotton	Hydromechanics	Scientific Instruments
Cutlery	Internal Combustion Engines	Shipbuilding
Drop Forging	Iron and Steel	Spring
Electrical	Jute	Steel Castings
Felt	Lace	Tar
Files	Launderers	Timber
Flour	Leather	Water
Food	Lime	Whiting
Fruit and Vegetable Canning	Linen	Wool
Furniture	Motor	

[1]This was the situation in 1961.

Table 1. BASIC TECHNOLOGIES

Biological technology
Agriculture
Forestry
Fishing

Mining technology
Ores
Oil
Coal
Gas

Chemical technology
Chemicals
Polymers
Metals

Materials technology
Plastics
Glass
Metals
Ceramics

Energy technology
Gas
Steam raising
Electricity
Nuclear energy

Food technologies

Environmental technology
Building
Housing
Lighting
Heating and ventilation
Acoustics

Transport technology
Road
Rail
Air
Sea
Space

Communications technology
Radio
Telegraphy
Printing

One approach is to classify technologies in relation to man's needs, in which case we achieve a measure of simplification as shown in Table 1.

Table 1 gives only examples, but serves to show how technologies can be grouped on a more rational basis. Some of these major technologies are already well recognized—for example, mining, food and chemical technologies. Others, such as materials technology[1] and environmental technology, have not attained the same recognition.

Materials technology

Let us take one example—materials technology—and consider it in a little more detail in order to demonstrate that certain fundamental principles can be seen to apply to a number of technologies which at the moment are considered to be quite separate.

This is a field where there should be great possibilities of cross-fertilization and interaction, for example, in the manufacture of intermediate raw materials, such as plastics, glass, metals, bricks or paper. If it can be accepted that this is, in fact, but one large technology, this will already represent an enormous simplification in the technological field. Can this statement be justified?

There is a unity about simple and composite solid materials which is as fundamental as the unity which exists in the science of chemistry. The unity in chemistry is based on the concept of the atom and the molecule. The unity in materials science is based on the concept of a solid, since all solids by definition have certain features in common with all other solids. These features are the physical properties such as tensile strength, rigidity and hardness which determine whether an object is a solid or not. That there is a fundamental science of materials has only recently been recognized. It is true that there was already a considerable body of knowledge from metallurgy and crystallography which was waiting to be pressed into service, but the subject of materials science had not been investigated in a systematic way.

If materials science is the investigation of the properties of all solid materials, with the view of relating these properties to the ultimate molecular structure, there must also be a subject which we can call materials technology which deals with the fabrication and processing of these materials. Furthermore, since the physical properties of a solid are intimately bound up with the way in which it is made, it will be very difficult to draw a sharp line between materials science and technology. There are clearly two skeins or threads connecting together different branches of materials technology, (*a*) a process skein and (*b*) a product skein. Let us consider the process skein to begin with.

[1]Materials technology has made considerable strides since this was written. L. H.

Process skeins—unit-forming processes

Ductile materials. A simple starting point is the processing of ductile and plastic materials—metals, thermoplastics and inorganic glasses. Inorganic glasses are brittle at ambient temperatures, but are plastic at, say, 500° C. Metals and thermoplastics are not ductile at very low temperatures, but become ductile in the temperature-range 0–150° C. The property of ductility is, in fact, a function of temperature. Since similar processes are used for fabricating these materials, one can introduce the concept of 'unit forming processes' to describe them. Table 2 shows

Table 2. UNIT FORMING PROCESSES

Ductile and plastic materials

	Metals	*Thermo-plastics*	*Inorganic glasses*
(1) *Forming Processes*			
Melt Processes			
Sintering	+	+	+
Casting	+	−	+
Flow Processes			
Moulding	+	+	+
Extrusion	+	+	+
Drawing	+	+	+
Stretching	−	+	−
Rolling/forging	+	+	−
Beating	+	−	−
Size Reduction			
Grinding	+	+	+
(2) *Structure-modifying Processes*			
Mixing Processes			
Alloying	+	+	−
Dispersion	+	+	+
Expanding	+	+	+
Surface Processes			
Case hardening	+	−	−
Surface treatment	+	+	+
Surface coating	+	+	+
Lamination	+	+	−
Heat Treatment Processes			
Annealing	+	+	+
Quenching	+	+	+

some processes which are in normal commercial use with these materials, from which it will be seen that similar processes are used, even though the temperature used varies. These processes divide themselves into true geometrical forming processes, and processes which set out to change the micro- and macrostructure of the material.

Although on an atomic or molecular scale the structures of these materials differ—from ordered crystalline lattices containing regions of disorder such as metals, to amorphous structures which show little order such as some polymers—they nevertheless show basic similarities in the ductile stage. In all cases, energy is required in order to change the physical form of the product. This work is required to overcome intermolecular forces, and in some cases chemical bonds are broken in the process. If the molecules are large, as in the case of thermoplastics, the molecular orientation may be changed. In all cases, stresses may be set up in the product which may affect its physical properties, and these may have to be removed.

It will be seen that processes which have grown up in the older technologies of glasses and metals are being applied in many cases to thermoplastics (this shows the scope for the simplest form of invention—invention by analogy). Fig. 1 shows the manufacture of a thermoplastic monofilament and Fig. 2 the manufacture of plastic bottles. There has been an obvious interaction here, although it is not complete. It is surprising, for example, that three-dimensionally expanded metals (to quote one example) have not yet been developed commercially. There are other new developments in the field of forming processes which have not yet been spread to all ductile materials, for example, extrusion accompanied by air blowing, the float glass process, impact extrusion and explosive forming.

Chemosetting materials. It will be seen that there is ample justification for studying unit-forming processes as a class, particularly since the concept of unit-forming processes can be further extended to other materials which at an earlier stage of manufacture will flow like plastic materials. These include bricks, ceramics, many thermosetting resins, rubber, concrete—the list is very long. This class of material is processed at some stage as highly viscous, non-Newtonian liquids which are shaped to the desired form. After they have been shaped, they are usually (but not always) heated in order to cure or set them, after which they are no longer ductile at any temperature. The transition from the liquid to the solid state is the result of a chemical reaction which is in sharp distinction to the class of ductile materials shown in the earlier table. This second class of material I shall call 'chemosetting'. Chemosets in the liquid state may be homogeneous (as raw rubbers) or dispersions (as concrete), and the chemical reactions which are responsible for achieving

1 Extrusion of plastic monofilament. This is followed by quenching and hot drawing

2 Photomicrograph of cell structure of expanded polystyrene (× 150)

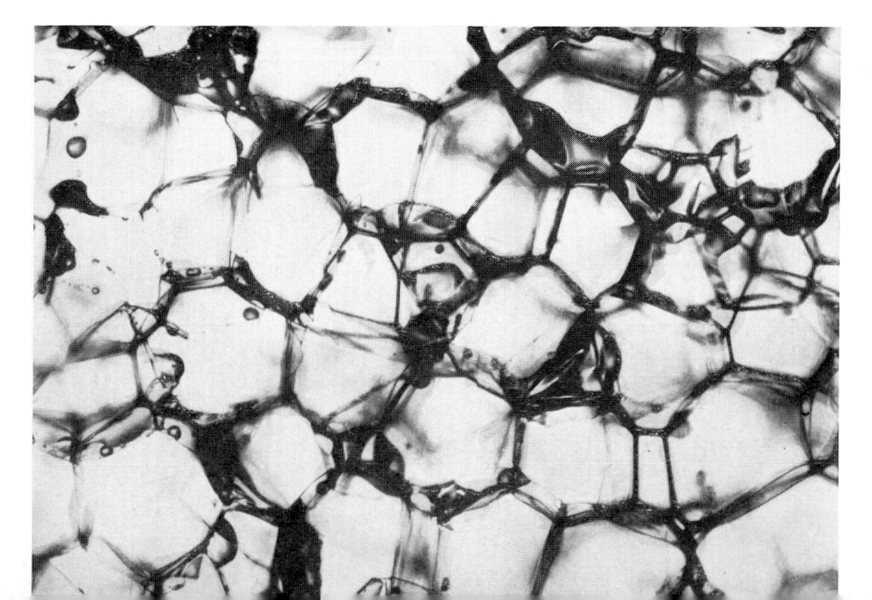

[*To face p.* 144

3 Blowing of plastic bottles, showing a bottle being removed from the mould. The extruder, which produces a hot 'parison' tube, is shown on the right

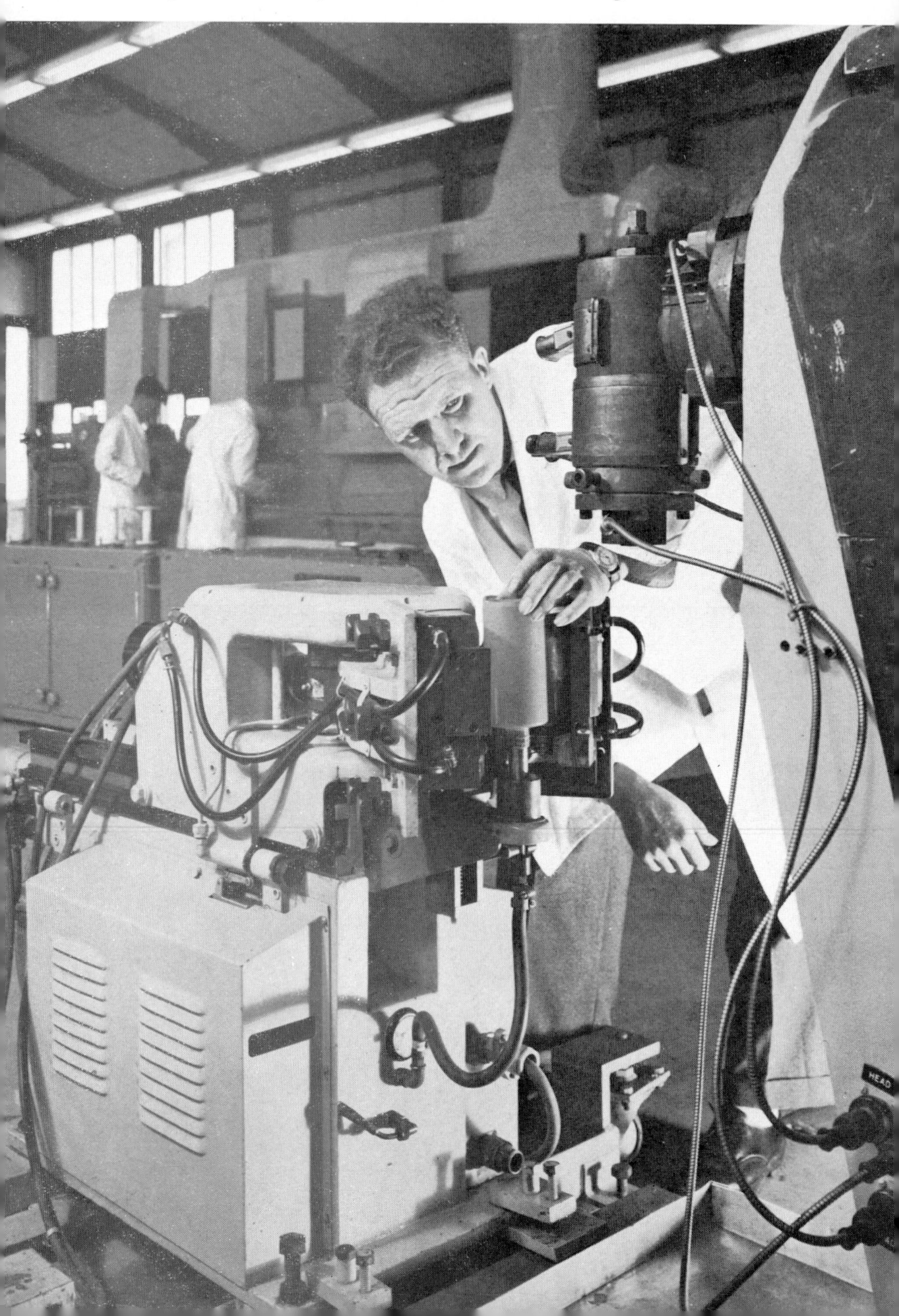

the solid state are diverse—from the formation of carbon–sulphur bonds (in the case of rubber) to the formation of aluminates and silicates (in the case of concrete).

It is clear that a large number of unit-forming processes which are utilized for plastic materials can be used for chemosets, and vice versa. However, this analogy between bricks and ceramics on one hand, and metals or glasses on the other, has not been clearly seen. In fact, these have usually been regarded as being completely different classes of materials, which has inhibited the cross-fertilization of ideas which we are looking for. On general grounds it can be claimed that it will repay the brick technologist to study metals processing, for example, and vice versa.

Filament processes. Clear analogies also exist in the field of weaving. All the materials shown in Table 2 will form filaments which can be spun or woven. Woven metals, glasses and thermoplastics (like nylon, terylene and polypropylene) are important commercially. There has been very little interest in weaving chemosets, although this could be done. Presumably, the reason has been that woven materials in the great majority of cases are required to be flexible, and chemosets are usually rigid. However, since glass (which is a very rigid material) is woven commercially, and rubber (which is a chemoset and very flexible) is also woven, it will be seen that the weaving of chemosets might repay study in special cases.

Matting processes. The formation of a mat or web—made up of fine filaments—is of importance in the manufacture of paper, and of growing importance in the case of non-woven fibres. Cellulose fibres, from which paper is made, are produced from wood by chemical digestions and extractions which remove the non-cellulosic materials, such as lignin. Their approximate dimensions are:

	Length	*Width*
Softwood	3–5 mm.	40μ
Hardwood	1–3 mm.	25μ

These fibres are thus very long and thin. The manufacture of paper and board depends on the fact that these fibres can readily be dispersed to form a suspension in water. When this suspension is filtered, a fibrous mat is formed which, on rolling and drying, produces a coherent sheet. This sheet can be built up in layers to produce a thick board of considerable mechanical strength. Superior mechanical properties can be obtained by impregnating this board with thermosetting materials such as ureaformaldehyde resins, which replace the air between the fibres by a rigid polymer.

The binding forces between the fibres in paper occur at the points where the fibres touch. Since the fibres are made up of cellulose, the binding consists of hydrogen bonds between the oxygen atom of a glucose unit in one fibre and a hydrogen atom of a glucose unit in an adjacent fibre. The result is a closely knit network of fibres.

It is apparent that a web or mat can be produced from any fibres of the correct geometry (that is, a high length/diameter ratio) if some self-bonding mechanism exists (as with paper) or some other bonding mechanism can be introduced, for example—the use of an adhesive. The key to using matting processes in a more general way is to recognize that the geometry of the system is not confined to cellulose fibres and the bonding forces are not restricted to hydrogen bonds. This has already been recognized in the case of non-woven fabrics, but the principle should be capable of extension.

Product skeins

Materials may be simple or complex on a macroscopic scale. The simpler structures like metals, glasses or organic polymers may show either long-term or short-term order on a molecular or atomic scale. It is one task of materials science to relate observed physical properties to molecular structure, and good progress has been made in the past twenty years in these fields.

There are, on the other hand, a large number of solids which are complex on a macroscopic scale. A typical example is expanded polystyrene (Fig. 3 facing p. 145). Table 3 gives a few examples of such materials.

Table 3. SOME COMPOSITES WHICH CONSIST OF TWO OR MORE PHASES

	Continuous phase	*Disperse phase*
Concrete	Cement	Sand and gravel
Bitumen aggregates	Bitumen	Stone and air
Filled thermoplastics	Linear polymer	Inorganic filler
Reinforced rubbers	Cross-linked polymer	Carbon black, silica
Asbestos cement	Cement	Asbestos fibres
Laminates	*Two continuous phases*	
Glass fibre/resin systems	Cross-linked polymer	Glass fibres

One of the important features of these composite materials is their geometry, and phase relationship.[1] They usually comprise a continuous phase and one or more disperse phases. Examples of composite materials

[1]See also Chapter I, *Composite Materials*, Elsevier, 1966, edited L. Holliday.

with more than one continuous phase are rare, although they do exist (an open polyurethane foam has a continuous gas phase and a continuous polymer phase; expanded polystyrene, which has a closed pore structure, has a disperse gas phase and a continuous polymer phase).

Some geometrical factors: In understanding the properties of composite materials it is important to consider those aspects which are affected by the geometry of the system. This point can be illustrated by taking a particular example, although the approach is a general one. Let us consider a filled thermoplastic in which a thermoplastic material like polyethylene constitutes the continuous phase, and a filler like chalk or carbon black constitutes the disperse phase. The geometry is defined by such factors as particle size and shape, volume fraction of the disperse phase, size and concentration distribution, orientation if the particles are non-spherical, etc. The geometrical parameters are the same in a concrete road or a bitumen aggregate. If p_s is any physical property of the composite material, then:

$$p_s = f(p_a, p_b, G_b, V_b,)$$

where p_a is the relevant physical property of continuous phase A; p_b is the analogous physical property of disperse phase B; G_b is a term which allows for the effect of the geometrical parameters of phase B on the properties; V_b is the volume fraction or concentration of phase B. This is for a two 'phase' system (it should be noted that these are not Gibbsian phases).

Three general points can be made about the effect of the geometry of the phases on the properties of composite materials: (1) the properties of composite materials are closely bound up with their geometry, (2) any composite may theoretically exist with any geometrical arrangement, (3) the effect of the geometry of phase arrangements is broadly similar in different systems.

There are one or two physical properties which are not affected by geometrical factors—for example density and specific heat. These are additive properties. However, it is the effect of geometrical terms on other non-additive properties which makes the study of composite materials so challenging.

The magnitude and effect of the term G_b depends on the particle size and surface area, and on the intermolecular forces at the interface between the particles and the continuous phase. In general, it increases as the particle size gets smaller. It is evident that this ability to change the physical properties of the system by modifying the geometry confers a new degree of freedom on composite materials. In addition, it is possible to modify the intermolecular forces at the interface by coating the particles before they are incorporated into the matrix. This is done in such different fields as thermoplastics and bitumen aggregates.

In certain special cases, a particle-particle interaction may occur which may affect properties. A typical example is in the reinforcement of rubber with carbon black or silica, where the particle size is below 1 micron. At below 10% by volume, each particle is operating independently. As the volume concentration is increased, the particles begin to form filament-like aggregates and the particle-particle interaction comes into play. This change in geometry leads to an increase in the electrical conductivity of the rubber.

Conclusions

These illustrations drawn from the field of materials technology illustrate the thesis—that benefits accrue from searching for the fundamental principles in individual technologies and for the relationships between them. This can only come from adopting a more analytical approach to technology as a whole, and by encouraging technologists to look beyond their individual specialities. What can be done to improve the situation?

(1) We should first look to the universities which have technological departments, and to the colleges of advanced technology, to bring together their technological departments into the largest possible units. As an example, instead of having in one university twenty professors of technological subjects each the head of an independent department, one should have a few large departments of technology, each with a number of professors. This is the way in which the Manchester College of Science and Technology is evolving. The department which now looks after textile chemistry and paper technology will in the future include polymer technology. We also need some professors of technology who are not concerned with narrow specialist fields, but who are concerned with industrial research and development as a whole, and with the philosophy of industrial research and development.

(2) There are too many technological societies and institutions, and too many technological journals. Some of these should be amalgamated.

(3) There is, in addition, a great need to cut down the number of industrial research associations and to bring them together into larger units. At the moment these research associations are scattered all over Britain in splinter groups. To have too many individual research

associations means that the basic and fundamental research is frequently being carried out by teams which are too small to be really effective. The Department of Scientific and Industrial Research is aware of this fact, but will have a formidable task to improve the present situation. The situation in Holland, with its Toegepast Natuurwetenschappelijk Onderzoek Institutes, represents a pattern which Britain might follow. Most of the Toegepast Natuurwetenschappelijk Onderzoek Institutes are grouped together in one large laboratory complex, and this laboratory complex is situated on the campus of the technical university at Delft. Thus not only do the devotees of specialist technologies rub shoulders with each other but they also rub shoulders with the university scientists.

The Ministry of Technology, as a major spender of public research funds, has probably the key responsibility to promote the interaction of technologies. It is keenly aware of these responsibilities; but it will have to work hard even to stay abreast of a situation which daily beomes more complex.

15

JOHN HEARLE

Materials Science and Technology

INTRODUCTION

The importance of materials

The use of materials is central to all technology. The rocket technologist may calculate the thrust needed or define the controls which must be used; the computer technologist may specify the functional operations; the electronic circuit designer may think of the current and voltage relations; the architect may design a building; even the artist or musician may conceive their creations: all these things can be done in the abstract, but for execution of any of the plans real materials must be used. With other technologies, such as chemical engineering, metallurgy, textile technology and much of mechanical and civil engineering, *it is virtually impossible to isolate any aspect of the subject* which is not a direct materials problem. Ultimately the solution of any technological endeavour can be reduced to putting the right material in the right place.

Materials science is thus a meeting-ground for many technologies. There are others such as the provision of power, instrumentation and control, probability and statistics, the similarity of mathematical forms, and the application of the laws of mechanics. These are all areas where the practitioners of different technologies can profit by common discussion. None is more important than the provision of materials with the properties needed to do the job.

New materials and advancing technology

We can see in materials science an immediate interaction in technological advance. New materials generate new technical possibilities, and so new industries arise; while, contrariwise, the demands of advancing technologies force the materials technologist to develop new materials. Sometimes the new material triggers the creation of a new utilization technology, and sometimes the demands of an advancing technology triggers the production of a new material.

This sort of interaction is seen in the relation between electronic engineering and semi-conductors, between fuel technology and rockets, or between aircraft design and advances in metallurgy. It is seen in the development of polymer technology in the last forty years, which has led to the vast new industries of plastics, man-made fibres and synthetic rubbers: these in turn have influenced many other technologies—building, adhesives, textiles, tyres, engineering, appliances, furniture, packaging, to name but a few—while, on the other hand, the demands of space technology have recently led to important advances in high-temperature polymer technology. At the frontiers of advancing technology, there is a ferment of ideas associated with advances in materials science.

Older technologies: the creation of new demand

In well-established industries using readily available and well-known materials, the problems of materials technology may not be so acute. The materials available may seem to meet all the technical requirements; and the designer can get by for a time without too much thought about materials—merely selecting them as components on the basis of past experience or from a cursory check of tables of standard products. Even here, advances in materials technology must be watched, if for no other reason than in order to ensure that the material being used is the most economical. But, surprisingly, new materials often generate new and unexpected technical demands.

The advent of synthetic fibres provides a simple example. When nylon was introduced in 1938, its obvious technical advantage was toughness, and it was first used where there was an unsatisfied demand for this quality: stronger ladies' stockings, harder wearing socks and better parachute fabrics were among the first uses. But then the development began to follow lines which would not have been predicted by a textile technologist in 1938. Even the requirements in ladies' stockings shifted from long life to extreme fineness—the demands of glamour outweighing the demands of efficiency! And then, with nylon and also the polyester and acrylic fibres which followed, new ease-of-care, drip-dry, wash-and-wear, crease-resistant and pleat-retaining properties were achieved in textile fabrics as a result of the heat-setting characteristics of synthetic fibres. There had been no great public demand for this: prior to 1945, the public had accepted the attributes of a cotton shirt or a wool suit as satisfactory. But once we met the advantages of the new materials, we realized how much we wanted the new properties.

As a consequence, the cotton, wool and rayon technologists had to set to, and find ways of achieving similar properties in fabrics made from these fibres. Resin finishes which would yield drip-dry cottons, and chemical treatments which would set wool fabrics were discovered. Scientifically there is little reason why these processes could not have been discovered in the great advances in the chemical finishing of textiles in the second half of the last century, or through the work of the strong British textile research associations established around 1920. But it was not until the new material had created the new demand that the problems were tackled and solved. The whole process has been repeated following the enormously successful introduction of stretch yarns made from synthetic fibres: stretch cotton and stretch wool are following. All this is part of a revolution in textile technology, more fundamental than the industrial revolution which brought power to the machines but did not change the materials; and it has come about as a result of interaction between chemical technology, polymer technology, man-made fibre technology and traditional textile technology—interaction, too, between mechanical and chemical aspects of fibre and fabric technology.

Materials sciences

The problems which arise between materials producing, materials processing and materials using technologies make one group of interactions related to different stages in the life of a particular material. But what about interactions between the technologies of different materials?

Ironically, the various materials technologies have developed with little contact between one another. Although they may have had mutual associates, the metallurgist and the glass technologist, the ceramicist and the textile technologist have not often met.

The lack of contact between materials technologists mattered little as long as each industry was run mainly on a craft basis, utilizing traditional recipes and procedures. The empirical cookery involved in the ageing and ripening of the cellulose solution used in rayon production is of little relevance to the empirical cookery of the iron smelter. It is only with the application of science, that a basis for useful contact between materials technologies becomes established. The understanding of the chemistry and of the macroscopic physical behaviour of materials dates from the days of Newton, Boyle, Hooke, Lavoisier, Dalton, Kekulé, Poiseuille, Faraday and Clerk Maxwell; but it is only in the last fifty years that we have really come to understand the fundamental nature of materials. Even today, although we know a lot about gases, crystalline solids and rubbers, and have mathematical theories of their

1 DISCONTINUITY AS SOURCE OF WEAKNESS
Stress concentration on a beam with rectangular notches as displayed by photo-elasticity (courtesy: Professor J. P. den Hartog, M.I.T.)

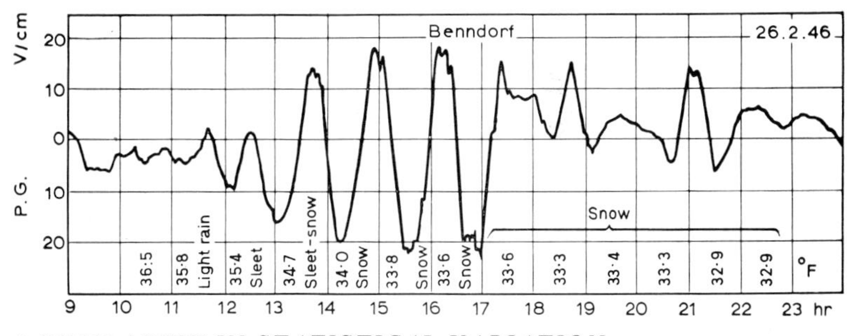

2 SIMILARITY IN STATISTICAL VARIATION
(a) Wave pattern of potential gradient during snow (courtesy: J. A. Chalmers, 'Atmosphere Electricity', Pergamon Press)

(b) Variation of yarn thickness (from 'Principles of Textile Testing', by J. E. Booth. A. Heywood book distributed by Iliffe Books Ltd.)

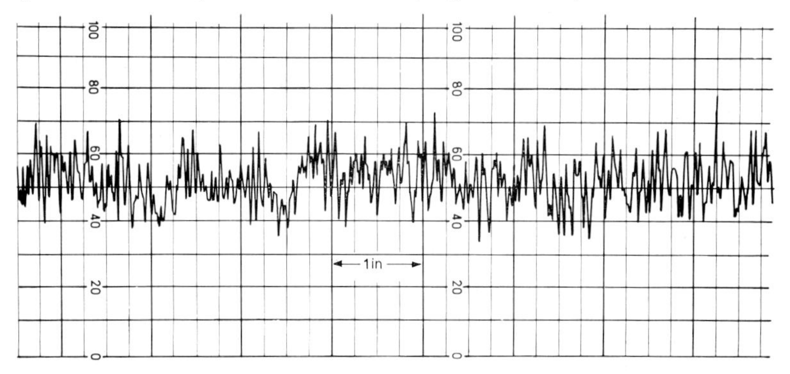

3 SIMILARITY BETWEEN METALS AND POLYMERS
(*a*) *Electron micrograph of single crystal of gold* (*courtesy*: *Dr. Natsu Uyeda, Kyoto University*)

(*b*) *Electron micrograph of single crystal of poly-oxy methylene* (*courtesy of Professor P. H. Geil, Case Institute of Technology*)

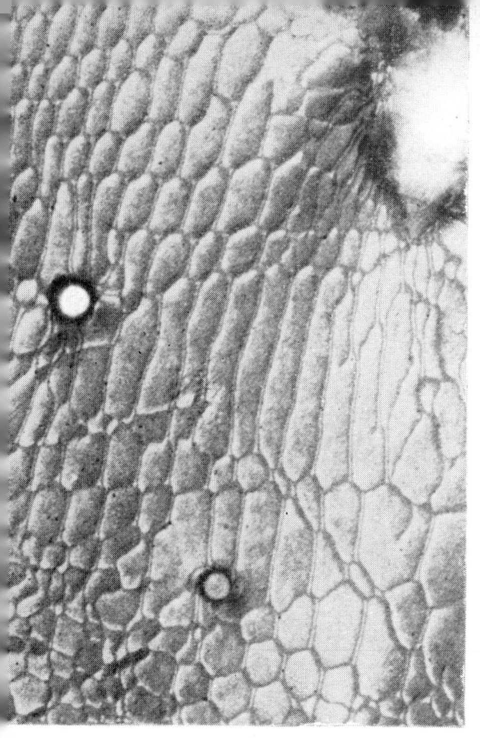

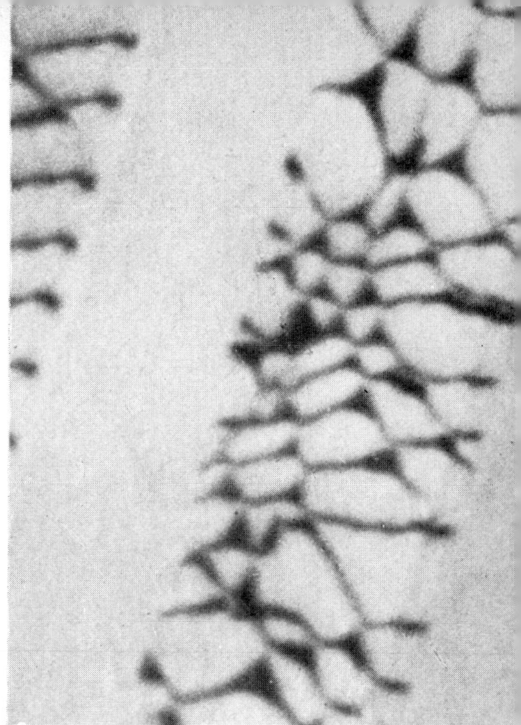

(*c*) *Dislocation network in polyethylene crystals* (*courtesy*: *P. H. Lindenmeyer, Chemstrand Research Center*)

(*d*) *Dislocations in stainless steel* (*courtesy*: *P. B. Hirsch, Cavendish Laboratory, Cambridge University*)

4 SIMILARITY AT DIFFERENT SCALES
(*a*) *Single cotton fibre* (*U.S.D.A. photo by Southern Utilization Research and Development Division*)

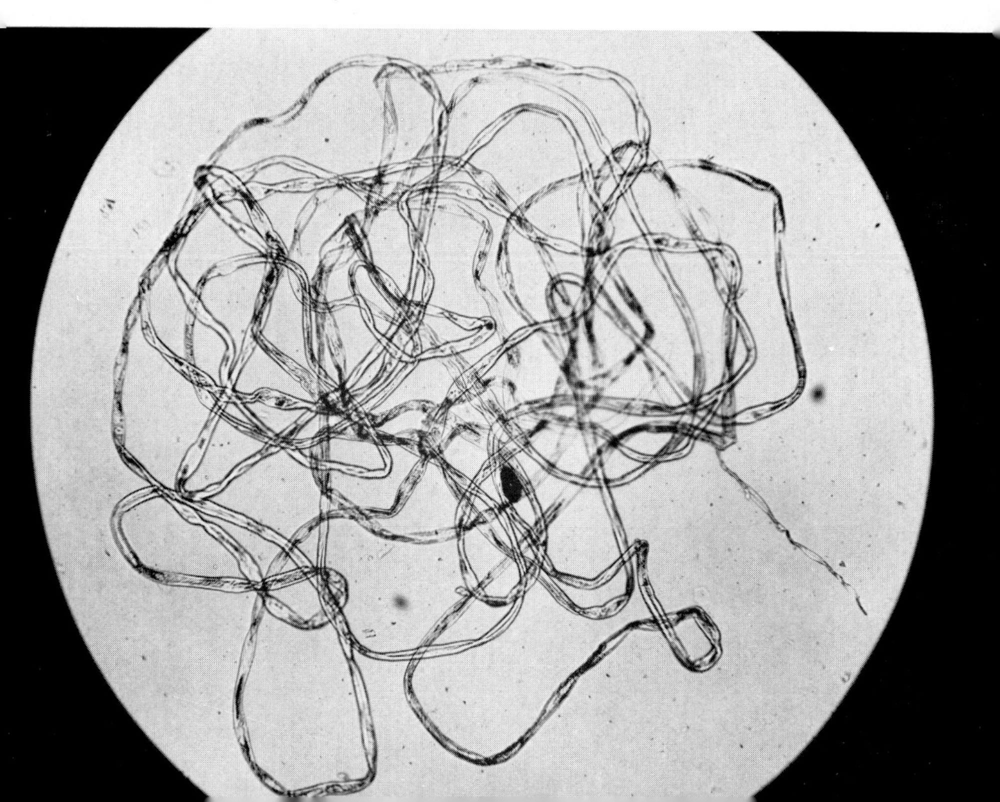

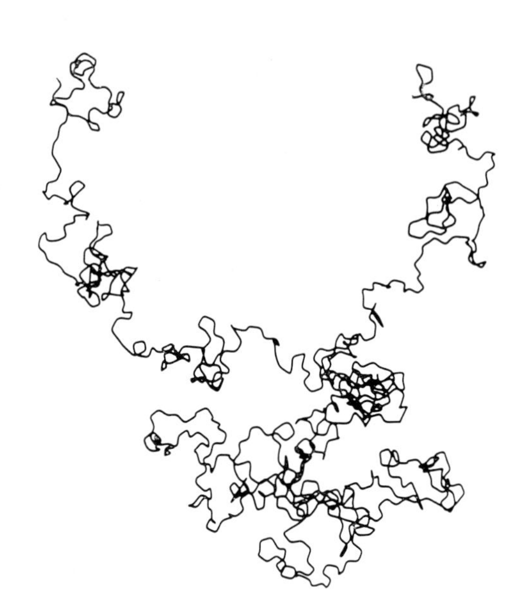

(b) Model of a single rubber molecule (courtesy: Dr. L. R. G. Terloar, Manchester Institute of Science and Technology)

(c) Cell-wall of seaweed, Cladophora rupestris. Electron micrograph (courtesy: Professor R. D. Preston, Leeds University)

(d) A non-woven fabric (courtesy: Dr. S. H. Zeronian, Manchester Institute of Science and Technology

behaviour, we are still very ignorant about liquids and glassy amorphous solids.

At first, too, as scientists looked at the problems of industrial materials, there was so much to study that each materials science could develop on its own. A basic framework of knowledge had to be established. But now as a result of the advances in pure science and in the applied sciences of various materials, contact between materials scientists is needed and is likely to yield surprising benefits. Already there are examples which can be quoted.

ILLUSTRATIONS

Continuity and discontinuity

In the materials of construction, strength is the most obvious technological requirement. Strength comes from continuity of structure. In metals we have a continuous band of electrons holding the atoms together, and in polymers we have a continuous network or chain of covalent chemical bonds. In strong materials whose structure is not so well known, this provides a clue about what we must look for. Thus in glasses there is probably a network structure though this is not as well defined as in polymers. In crystals of small molecules, the extent to which one can get strength depends on how closely the molecules can pack together in order to develop a degree of continuity in intermolecular attractions.

Conversely, discontinuity is a source of weakness. Materials fail at flaws. Here Griffith's classical treatment of the propagation of fracture from a crack has set off a train of interactions in technology. The Griffith criterion has been applied and modified in glasses, metals, polymers and many other materials. As long as one is dealing with a pure homogeneous flawless material, one's gaze can be narrower: the properties of the particular assembly of atoms are all that matter. The modulus, that is the force needed to produce a given small strain, can be calculated from the deformation characteristics of the particular atomic bonds in the structure; and the result will usually agree well with the values for real materials. But calculations of strength will always yield too high a value, usually orders of magnitude greater than the strength of real materials. It is the unusual points of weakness that must be looked at, and not the behaviour of the bulk of the material. In studies of the rupture of real materials, we can be helped by the relevant work in the technology of all materials. The behaviour of materials at discontinuities is a general problem (Fig. 1). A recent book on *Fracture Processes in Polymeric Solids* draws heavily on earlier work in metals and glass. On the other side, Orowan and McClintock at M.I.T. have studied the pattern of ridges produced in the fracture of gelatin and the cracks developed during the flexural fatigue of plasticine, and have used the results to explain the similar effects which occur on a much smaller scale in metals.

The importance of flaws as a source of weakness has led to the recent searches for flawless materials: perfect single crystals. Diamond is the classic naturally occurring example; but now we have single crystal whiskers of metals and of materials like silicon carbide. These are fibrous in form, and in their application lessons can be learnt from the old-established fibre technologies of textiles and paper.

Curiously enough, discontinuity can also be a source of strength. It can spread out the forces on a material; it can prevent dangerous stress concentrations; it can interrupt the progress of a crack. Whereas a continuous material may be able to resist very large loads, it is liable to be brittle and to shatter under conditions where a material with the right sort of discontinuity would yield, but would not break. The crystal defects in metals, the amorphous regions in crystalline polymers and the rubber which can be dispersed in polystyrene in order to toughen it perform this function.

In dealing with a real materials system, the technologist has to keep in mind two separate but interrelated aspects: firstly, the responses of each part of the system to the local stress; and secondly the influence which this has on the distribution of stress through the system. For example, the absorption of water by cellulose fibres always breaks cross-links and makes it easier for the molecules to slide over one another: but, in rayon, with short molecules, this lowers the strength; whereas, in cotton, with longer molecules, where breakage by molecular slip is not important, the more uniform distribution of stress results in a higher strength. Lessons like this illuminate our understanding of materials in general.

Another area where work with different materials has interacted is in the statistical problems of failure. Lawrence Balls—one of the first great technologists of the cotton industry—appreciated the 'weak-link effect' in determining the strength of cotton yarn. Then, in 1929, Peirce at the Shirley Institute treated the problem statistically, dealing both with the series problem of a sequence of elements of different strength and the related parallel problem of a bundle of threads. As one follows the subject, the contributions come from Weibull and Irwin on metals, leading into the whole problem of fatigue in engineering materials; from Spencer-Smith again on textile yarns, dealing with the effect of correlation in strength between neighbouring elements; from Coleman on fibres and polymers, taking account of the time-dependent effects; and from Freudenthal and Gumbel in their work on extreme value statistics, which demonstrates the relevance of the problem in any technological field where one is interested in the rare occurrences at one end of a frequency distribution. Work on cotton yarns could become relevant to work on the interruption of radio control in space: the statistical problems are similar (Fig. 2). The intensity of interruption varies from hour to hour, day to day and year to year as a result of the superposition of several regular and random effects: the variation of thickness or strength of a yarn along its length similarly results from a superposition of different effects.

Polymers and metals; glasses and liquids

Ten years ago most scientists concerned with either material would have said that polymers and metals were as different as the proverbial 'chalk and cheese'. But recently Malcolm Williams of Chemstrand Research Centre opened a lecture at M.I.T. by presenting pairs of slides, and inviting the audience to decide which were from metals and which were from crystalline polymers (Fig. 3). There was close similarity in the morphological forms shown in electron micrographs and in the shape of curves of mechanical properties. The link between the two is the way in which crystallization occurs. The chief determining factors in crystal growth are the critical size of nuclei, the tendency to minimize free energy and the mass and heat transfer in the region of the growing crystal. These are general effects and they result in similar forms. If crystallization starts in several places we get a domain structure. Imperfections appear as defects and dislocations in the crystal. On applying a force, there is first a small elastic deformation of the crystal itself; but then as the force builds up, the defects start to move through the system, like a ridge being pushed along in a carpet; crystal planes slide over one another, and we get yielding and permanent deformation. This happens in the drawing of films, metals and fibres.

The polymer scientist used to think of crystalline polymers as composed of small crystalline regions embedded in a non-crystalline matrix, and consider the deformations of the two parts separately. Now he is realizing that it is also possible to think of materials in the same way as the metallurgist, and consider polymers as a continuous crystalline material loaded with defects. Of course, the behaviour of metals and polymers is not identical: in polymers the atoms are connected in long chains, and this both influences the type of movement which is possible and is likely to lead to larger regions of disorder. Consequently there is still value in the older ideas, as well as the newer ones coming in from metallurgy.

While crystalline polymers have much in common with metals, the study of the technology of amorphous polymers will benefit from work on glasses and liquids. The extent to which there is some degree of order in these systems is an important unsolved problem. This is turn reacts on the behaviour of crystalline materials, since the existence of order in the melt will influence the detailed structure of the crystalline solid which is formed. An understanding of the behaviour of a wholly amorphous material may also be a help in understanding more complicated polycrystalline materials: studies of the cold-drawing of amorphous polymers such as polystyrene are being carried out as a lead to the understanding of drawing of synthetic fibres.

Fibrous systems

In living organisms, fibres are of great importance: nerves, muscle fibres and tendons all help to make the body work. Man has long utilized fibres in textiles and paper. Fibres are strong and flexible—two properties which are often opposed, for if you strengthen a structure you usually make it more rigid. In a well-designed fibre system, you can allow the fibres to act independently to give freedom of movement, but cause them to combine to resist rupture.

The flexibility of fibres is to be expected, because they are so fine, sometimes less than ten wavelengths of light in diameter; but their strength is greater than might be expected. Whereas sheet glass has a strength of about 2,000 lb. per square inch, commercial glass fibres are nearly a hundred times stronger, and carefully prepared undamaged glass fibres break at 500,000 lb. per square inch. This is due to the critical dependence of strength on cracks and other flaws—you cannot have a deep crack in a fibre!

Consider a bundle of 1,000 glass fibres. If one fibre is broken, the strength is reduced by 0.1%; but a comparable crack in the surface of an equivalent glass rod would cause a catastrophic drop in strength. Furthermore, if there is some cohesion, due to friction or a binding material between the fibres, then a fibre which is broken in one place will contribute to the strength elsewhere. The degree of cohesion has to be right: if it is too strong, the stress concentration will not be prevented, and the advantages of the fibrous system will be lost, while if it is too weak the whole fibre will slip.

The best-known practical realization of strong fibre reinforced systems is in reinforced plastics: cotton or paper in phenolic resins, and fibre glass in polyester resin. The plastics technologist is likely to be faced with a choice between woven and knitted fabrics, and with the other complexities of textile and paper technology.

Now there is also an interest in fibre reinforced metals. Rolls-Royce, for example, are investigating aluminium-coated quartz fibres which can be pressed up into blocks. They are having to solve the problems of melt spinning, just like any other fibre producer. Others are studying the possibilities of single crystal whisker fibres.

Apart from all the incidental mixing of technologies which comes from the uses of fibres in constructional materials, there is the fundamental problem of how fibre-reinforced materials behave. Their technology is not yet well understood. The commercially successful reinforced plastics have been produced by empirical trials, rather than designed on the basis of rational understanding. Theoretical and experimental investigation of a variety of systems is needed.

There is a wider unifying subject here in the structure and mechanics of fibrous systems. Wood and paper, woven and knitted textiles, cords and ropes, the new non-woven fabrics, fabrics coated with flexible thermoplastics, thermo-setting resins or metals reinforced with inextensible fibres, and concrete toughened by the addition of nylon fibres are all different systems; but there are analogous problems in the geometry and statistics of fibre arrangement and in mechanical, electrical, thermal, diffusion and optical behaviour. The acquisition of a facility in dealing with all the systems will come from studying them together.

Problems of scale

There are other useful analogies where the scale of a system is changed. Scale down a fibre assembly a thousand times and you have an assembly of polymer chain molecules; scale it down a hundred times, and you have the fine fibrillar structure which often occurs when polymers crystallize; but scale it up a thousand or more times and you have concrete reinforced with metal wires or rods (Fig. 4).

Theoretical or experimental results can be taken over, with care, from one problem to another. The understanding of rubber elasticity helps our understanding of non-woven fabrics. The well-proven analysis of the mechanics of twisted yarn has been applied in an analysis of the mechanics of single plant fibres.

Rheology and dynamic behaviour

Mechanical properties are time-dependent. This is always true, though it can be ignored when an elastic deformation is so much more rapid or a viscous deformation so much slower than the time-scale of ordinary events. In the many circumstances where time cannot be ignored, the subject of rheology brings together a diverse collection of scientists and technologists. The basic mathematical and experimental methods are the foundations of the subject; but the superstructure spreads out into metallurgy, polymer technology, oil technology, lubrication, adhesion, paper-making, textile technology, geophysics, physiology and medicine, soil mechanics and other applications.

We find in this subject too a link between mechanical and electrical properties of materials. The swinging of dipoles into alignment with an electric field is a mechanical action. So the dynamic response of a material to an alternating electric signal has very close similarity to the response to an alternating stress. Dynamic compliance (the reciprocal of modulus) is analogous to dielectric constant; mechanical creep is analogous to the build-up of electric polarization; and the effect of temperature in loosening up a structure is similar.

The experimental problems of rheology also tax the ingenuity of the electronic engineer, so that we find one of the most important schools of the rheology of liquids in a School of Electrical Engineering. Other schools are in Mathematics, Physics or Chemistry Departments as well as in many technological departments.

Dynamics of processing

It is one thing to study materials in the laboratory, or even to study them in use: it is another thing to study their behaviour in processing. Speed is then all-important. Polymer crystallization may take hours or weeks in the laboratory, but the man-made fibre being extruded in the factory moves through the crystallization zone at a high speed. A drill pierces metal in a fraction of a second. Large volumes of material flow through pipes at high speed.

In all these situations, the dynamics of processing must be considered. Consider the first example of the production of a man-made fibre. As it emerges from the spinneret, we have first the rheological problem of flow in a visco-elastic medium—within the tube, the molecules are oriented, but on emerging they spring back to a disoriented form, and we get a contraction, a bulging and a reduction in velocity. Then we get problems of hydrodynamics and aerodynamics, as the flow accelerates under gravity but is retarded by the drag of the surrounding gas. All the time, we have a heat-flow problem as the specimen cools; this leads to change in viscosity, and ultimately to solidification and perhaps to crystallization. Finally, there is the mechanical problem of winding up the yarn. If we want to take any measurements during the process, we are immediately led into complex problems of instrument engineering—how do you determine the temperature of a rapidly moving molten threadline, a few microns in diameter? And if we want to control the process, we have the problems of control engineering. Can the technology of man-made fibre production possibly be studied in isolation?

The same comment could be made about many chemical engineering and mechanical engineering processes. The dynamic problems inevitably bring in aspects of many technologies.

The textile industry

As final examples, we take two more limited topics. The first is the textile industry—or should it be industries? It used to be. Spinning, weaving, knitting and chemical finishing were all studied separately. Individual companies had a very narrow range of operation: they often dealt with only a specific aspect of processing of one type of fibre.

This has changed now—the textile technologist must know the whole field. He must be able to select the fibres, and determine the sequence of operations from fibre to finished product. Here we see not so much the interaction of technologies as the merging of several technologies into one, and with the non-woven fabrics coming very close also to paper technology.

Tyre-cords: a choice of materials

The other example concerns a choice between materials in a large industrial market with fairly clearly defined requirements. For use as tyre-cords there is a choice between cotton, rayon, nylon, polyester fibre, fibre glass and steel. All are being used—the natural fibre, the regenerated fibre, the synthetic fibres, the glass and the metal. This is an example of interaction by competition in use. The user must look at all the technologies; the supplier must watch the technology of his competitors.

Cotton used to be the material used, but in the 1940s it was replaced by rayon, except in bicycle tyres. Then nylon challenged rayon, and there is still a nicely poised balance of technical and economic factors. Incidentally the strength of rayon tyre-cords has been almost doubled in advances over a period of ten years, due to this competition. So far, the competition was within the textile industry, but with steel wire the competition came from outside textiles. Courtaulds hedged by acquiring a company supplying steel for this purpose! The technological and economic arguments about the different materials go on.

CONCLUSION

The advantages of interaction

In this essay, it has been shown how the materials technologies interact with other technologies in use, and in the methods used to process materials. These interactions are fairly obvious. The user has to handle many materials; and there is competition between materials from very different sources.

Less obvious is the value of interaction between the scientific studies of different materials. Work on other materials can be a useful source of ideas; and sometimes a detailed analysis can be taken over. But perhaps the most valuable general feature is that a comparative study of different materials enables the specific to be separated from the general. It is all too easy in dealing with a particular material to attribute phenomena to specific features: to ascribe the characteristic draw-ratio in synthetic fibres to some particular molecular transformation, whereas it is merely a result of adiabatic extension of material with a certain, common form of load-extension curves; or to attribute particular oblique lines of fracture to a particular crystal structure instead of to a stress distribution which would occur in all specimens of the same shape. Luder's bands, first found in metallic fracture, have reappeared in the literature of the fatigue failure of fibres. Or again, changes which were found in the nature of break of reinforced metal specimens as the specimen length was changed were found to be similar to effects which had been previously reported for textile yarns.

By studying the behaviour of a variety of materials, we can build up a coherent body of knowledge in place of an empirical compendium of unrelated facts. We now have the necessary scientific basis, though the complications of applying it to the behaviour of real materials—so different from the abstractions and specially simple examples beloved by the pure physicist—should not be underestimated. On the more practical side, there is much to be gained from collaboration and exchange of ideas in processing methods—cutting, moulding, drawing, forming and so on—and in instrumentation and control. As the use of materials becomes more and more a rational technology, and less pure industrial empiricism, the benefits of interaction among the materials technologies and with other technologies will grow. For this reason it is encouraging that materials scientists and technologists are increasingly co-operating in various centres and societies, so that the barriers between the technologies are coming down.

INDEX